Reading for Comprehension

Level **H**

To the Student

This book contains exciting articles for you to read and enjoy. They tell about real-life adventures, unusual animals, famous people, interesting places, and important events.

There are questions after each article to help you think about and remember what you have read. The last question will give you a chance to write about the topic of the article.

Comprehension means "understanding." Good readers comprehend what they read. You can become a better reader and writer as you go through this book and focus on understanding.

Continental

Credits

Editorial Development: Matt Baker, Beth Spencer

Editorial Support: Joyce Ober, Anthony Moore

Cover and Interior Design: Joan Herring

Illustrators: Pages 6, 7; 22, 23; 26, 27; 46, 47; 78, 79 Rob Williams
Pages 8, 9; 28, 29; 52, 53; 68, 69; 76, 77; 90, 91; 92, 93 Margaret Lindmark

Photo Credits: Front cover: *Bald eagle, saguaro cactus, giraffes:* www.photos.com; *clownfish:* www.istockphoto.com/redtwiggy; *Mt. Rushmore:* www.istockphoto.com/megasquib; *open book:* www.istockphoto.com/mstay; Pages 4, 5: www.wikipedia.org; Pages 10, 11: www.photos.com; Pages 12, 13: www.istockphoto.com/twhite; Pages 14, 15: www.photos.com; Pages 16, 17: Library of Congress Prints and Photographs Division, LC-USZ62-114266; Pages 18, 19: www.istockphoto.com/Dreef; Pages 20, 21: www.istockphoto.com/Mummu Media; Pages 24, 25: www.wikipedia.org; Pages 30, 31: www.photos.com; Pages 32, 33: www.wikipedia.org; Pages 36, 37: www.istockphoto.com; Pages 38, 39: www.photos.com; Pages 42, 43: www.wikipedia.org; Pages 44, 45: www.photos.com; Pages 48, 49: NASA; Pages 50, 51: www.photos.com; Pages 54, 55: www.istockphoto.com/NNehring; Pages 58, 59: www.photos.com; Pages 60, 61: www.istockphoto.com/benoitb; Pages 62, 63: www.photos.com; Pages 64, 65: www.wikipedia.org; Pages 70, 71: www.istockphoto.com/DarienP; Pages 72, 73: www.istockphoto.com/mjunior; Pages 74, 75: www.photos.com; Pages 80, 81: www.istockphoto.com/PEDRE; Pages 82, 83: www.photos.com; Pages 84, 85: www.photos.com; Pages 86, 87: www. wikipedia.org; Pages 88, 89: www.wikipedia.org; Pages 94, 95: www.photos.com

ISBN 978-0-8454-1687-7

Contents

What is America's oldest state capital?

1   Even people who know a lot about history have trouble guessing what city is America's oldest state capital. They assume that it must be in one of the first 13 states. The truth is that it is far to the west of those places. It is the capital of New Mexico: Santa Fe.

2   The modern city of Santa Fe was founded by the Spanish in 1609. That was more than 10 years before the pilgrims landed at Plymouth Rock. The history of the place goes back even further, though. Santa Fe was built on top of ancient Native American ruins. When the Spanish arrived, the Pueblo people had a number of villages in the area. They are believed to have been living there for about 600 years before the Spanish arrived. They live there to this day.

3   From the start, Santa Fe was a seat of government. However, power has changed hands many times. In 1680, the Spanish were driven out by the Pueblo people, but they returned 12 years later. In 1821, Mexico became independent from Spain. Santa Fe was now part of Mexico and was named the capital of the province of New Mexico. Mexico lost Santa Fe to the United States in 1846. The city became the capital of the U.S. territory of New Mexico. Finally, in 1912, New Mexico became a state, with Santa Fe as its capital.

4   When people visit Santa Fe today, they still see many signs of the city's long, lively history. The city has preserved historic buildings, and the Spanish–Pueblo style of architecture is still being used. Also, many of the cultures that have called the area home still live there. Santa Fe's rich cultural heritage makes it one of the country's most interesting places to visit.

Circle the correct answer for questions 1–5.
Write your answer to question 6 on a separate piece of paper.

1. Santa Fe has never belonged to _____.
   A Native Americans
   B England
   C Mexico
   D Spain

2. Which word in paragraph 3 means "center"?
   A seat
   B power
   C capital
   D territory

3. Which paragraph tells about the first people who lived in the Santa Fe area?
   A 1
   B 2
   C 3
   D 4

4. You can infer from the article that _____.
   A New Mexico was one of the first 13 states
   B Plymouth Rock once belonged to Mexico
   C some people in Santa Fe speak Spanish
   D Santa Fe was the capital of Spain

5. *Driven* can have the following meanings. Mark the meaning used in paragraph 3.
   A taken
   B forced
   C traveled
   D motivated

6. Use print and online resources to learn about the capital of your state. Write a brief history of the city.

Could another ice age happen?

1   For 2.5 million years, the Earth has been in a warm–cold cycle. Warm periods have been followed by times of cold. The cold parts of the cycle are called *ice ages.* For the last 15,000 years, the Earth has been warm. Lately, it has become warmer still. Everyone has heard about "global warming." Warnings have been issued that melting polar ice could cause sea levels to rise. Yet some scientists believe that another ice age may not be far off. And global warming might help begin it.

2   How could this be? In the 1980s, science found a way to study the Earth's past climate changes. Every year, a layer of ice is added to glaciers in Greenland. Scientists can read these layers like a tree's growth rings. A thicker layer means a colder year. Ice ages, these layers show, have followed brief periods of global warming. And they begin suddenly—possibly within just 10 years.

3   One reason this happens has to do with Atlantic Ocean currents. The Gulf Stream brings warm water northward from the equator. This is what keeps northern Europe warm. Warm water evaporates. This increases the salt level in the northern ocean. Saltier water sinks. A return current flowing deep in the ocean brings it back south.

4   This cycle usually happens every year. But what happens if global warming suddenly adds a lot of fresh water to the northern ocean? The flow of cold water southward stops. The warm current cannot flow northward. The result could be sudden cooling. It could affect the climate worldwide.

5   Scientists are *not* predicting a new ice age. They are merely describing what has happened before. But each of the Earth's warm periods has been followed by a cold one. When the present one ends, will people be prepared?

Circle the correct answer for questions 1–5.
Write your answer to question 6 on a separate piece of paper.

1. Scientists have learned about climate changes
   by studying _____.
   A ancient writings
   B the Gulf Stream
   C tree growth rings
   D glaciers in Greenland

2. Which word in paragraph 3 means "makes larger"?
   A evaporates
   B increases
   C currents
   D saltier

3. Which paragraph describes how global warming could set off an ice age?
   A 1
   B 2
   C 3
   D 4

4. What would *not* happen if global warming added a lot of fresh water to the
   northern ocean?
   A The climate would cool.
   B The flow of cold water south would stop.
   C The flow of warm water north would stop.
   D Greenland would have thinner layers of ice.

5. You can infer from the article that salt makes water _____.
   A fresh
   B freeze
   C heavy
   D evaporate

6. Suppose scientists knew for sure that an ice age would begin in 10 years. Write a
   list of steps for what you would do to prepare.

1   In 1990, Nelson Mandela was freed from prison. Four years later, he ran for president of South Africa. It was the first time that people of all races were allowed to vote in the country. Mandela won by a landslide and became the country's first black president.

2   When Mandela was born in 1918, South Africa was ruled by white people who denied others many basic rights. In 1948, things got even worse. Laws were passed that began the system of *apartheid* (a•PAR•tyt). Under apartheid, non-white people could not marry white people, work certain jobs, or even enter parts of the country without special permission.

3   Mandela refused to give in to apartheid. He insisted that he should have the same rights as any person. In the 1940s he helped found the African National Congress, or ANC, to oppose apartheid.

4   The South African government did not like anyone who opposed the country's laws. Many members of the ANC were arrested for standing up for their rights. One of them was Mandela. In 1962, he was sent to prison. He remained there for 27 years.

5   While he was in jail, Mandela became a symbol for equal rights in South Africa. Many times the government tried to make deals to release him. Every time, though, he said that he would not settle for anything less than equal rights. Finally, in 1990, South Africa gave in to his demands. Apartheid came to an end, and Nelson Mandela was free. Today, he remains an inspiration to people all over the world.

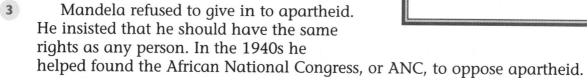

Circle the correct answer for questions 1–5.
Write your answer to question 6 on a separate piece of paper.

1. The article does *not* say that _____.
    A Nelson Mandela stayed in prison because he could write there
    B Nelson Mandela was elected president of South Africa
    C Nelson Mandela was one of the founders of the ANC
    D Nelson Mandela was in prison for many years

2. Which word in paragraph 4 means "stood against"?
    A arrested
    B opposed
    C standing
    D remained

3. Which paragraph explains what apartheid is?
    A 2   C 4
    B 3   D 5

4. You can infer from the article that _____.
    A Nelson Mandela did not stand up for his beliefs
    B Nelson Mandela's time in prison was not difficult
    C Nelson Mandela is not well known outside South Africa
    D Nelson Mandela knows that freedom sometimes has to be earned

5. *Found* can have the following meanings. Mark the meaning used in paragraph 3.
    A start
    B located
    C adopted
    D discovered

6. The article says that Nelson Mandela became a symbol for equal rights. That means that when people thought of him, they also thought of a larger cause. Can you think of another person who is a symbol for a cause? Write a short essay explaining why this person is so recognizable.

Can dolphins really talk?

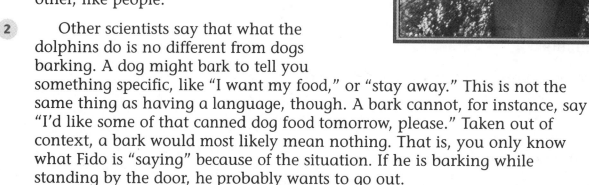

1   Like other animals, dolphins make noises. Most of these noises are clicks and whistles. Sometimes clicks come in a series that almost sounds like a code. Dolphins also make a great variety of other sounds, including barks and screeches. Sometimes, their noises seem to mimic other animals, such as ducks, fish, or even humans. Many dolphin sounds are outside of the range of human hearing. So, what do all these noises mean? Some scientists say dolphins are actually talking to each other, like people.

2   Other scientists say that what the dolphins do is no different from dogs barking. A dog might bark to tell you something specific, like "I want my food," or "stay away." This is not the same thing as having a language, though. A bark cannot, for instance, say "I'd like some of that canned dog food tomorrow, please." Taken out of context, a bark would most likely mean nothing. That is, you only know what Fido is "saying" because of the situation. If he is barking while standing by the door, he probably wants to go out.

3   Dolphins seem to be able to communicate in a way that goes beyond this. Experiments have been done in which dolphins in different tanks seemed to have conversations by telephone. They start to make sounds once the phone is turned on. Unlike dogs when they bark at each other, dolphins also seem to listen, because one is silent when the other is "talking."

4   So, do dolphins really talk? No one will be able to tell until people find a way to translate their sounds. While scientists are trying to do this, you can only imagine what talking with a dolphin would be like.

Reading for Comprehension

Circle the correct answer for questions 1–5.
Write your answer to question 6 on a separate piece of paper.

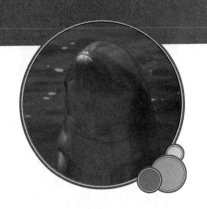

1. The article says that dolphins may be able to do all of
   the following *except* _____.

   A talk on the phone

   B whistle

   C write

   D bark

2. Which word in paragraph 1 means "imitate"?

   A code

   B range

   C make

   D mimic

3. Which paragraph tells the purposes of dogs' barking?

   A 1

   B 2

   C 3

   D 4

4. You can conclude from the article that _____.

   A some animals may be more like people than people think

   B scientists understand everything dolphins say

   C dogs have a real language, too

   D dolphins can talk to dogs

5. *Great* can have the following meanings. Mark the meaning used in paragraph 1.

   A wonderful

   B extreme

   C wide

   D far

6. Take the position that dolphins can communicate on a higher level than other
   animals. Write a letter to your science teacher to state your case. Use examples
   from the article to support your position.

1   *Kuumba* (koo•OOM•bah) is a Swahili word. It means "thinking of new ways to do things" in that African language. Maulana Karenga, an African American teacher, showed kuumba in 1966 when he started a new holiday, Kwanzaa. He wanted to teach African Americans about their long history as Africans and as Americans. Karenga thought that a holiday would be a good way for his people to celebrate both their past and their future. Kwanzaa lasts the whole week between Christmas and New Year's Day.

2   On the first day of Kwanzaa, a child lights a candle. Led by the child, everyone talks about *umoja,* one of the seven goals African Americans work toward. Umoja means "unity, or staying together."

3   Each of the next six days of Kwanzaa celebrates another African American goal. They are *kujichagulia* (acting and speaking for oneself), *ujima* (working together), *ujamaa* (buying goods and services from one another), *nia* (having a purpose for what one does), kuumba, and *imani* (believing in oneself).

4   Everyone brings something to share for the Kwanzaa feast on December 31. The food is spread out on a big *mkeka,* or mat, in the middle of the floor. The mat is often black, red, and green, colors found in many African flags.

5   The last day of Kwanzaa is probably the children's favorite. On this day, they receive presents. These are rewards for promises they have made and kept during the past year. Friends of other races are often invited to celebrate Kwanzaa. Sharing the holiday is a wonderful way to learn about the history and future of African Americans.

Circle the correct answer for questions 1–5.
Write your answer to question 6 on a separate piece of paper.

1. The article does *not* tell _____.
   A who Maulana Karenga is
   B how people dress for Kwanzaa
   C when gifts are given during Kwanzaa
   D how many days Kwanzaa is celebrated

2. Which word in paragraph 1 means "the record or story of past events"?
   A language
   B holiday
   C history
   D teacher

3. Which paragraph tells how Kwanzaa came about?
   A 1
   B 2
   C 3
   D 4

4. What happens after the Kwanzaa feast on December 31?
   A Children light candles.
   B Children receive presents.
   C Families celebrate ujima.
   D Families talk about umoja.

5. You can infer from the article that people who celebrate Kwanzaa _____.
   A do not celebrate Christmas
   B are proud of their African heritage
   C do not involve friends of other races
   D are not likely to involve children in the celebration

6. What is your favorite holiday? Write a short essay explaining the origin of the holiday.

1   Each year about 40,000 pounds of debris from space rains down on Earth. Most of the objects are no bigger than a grain of sand. They aren't even noticed. Yet from time to time, some bigger pieces fall from the sky. These could be the size of a baseball, truck, building, mountain, or even city.

2   In 1908, a comet, somewhere between 30 and 300 feet across, exploded over Siberia. Seven hundred square miles of forest were burned to the ground. The heat even burned the clothes of a person 60 miles away.

3   A huge asteroid, about half a mile across, passed Earth in 1989, missing by 700,000 miles. That may not seem close, but if it had come by just six hours later, it would have crashed into the planet. The result could have been tidal waves hundreds of feet high and fires destroying cities. A cloud of dust might have blocked out the sun for the next year. Without sun, crops wouldn't grow. There would have been no warning because no one saw the asteroid coming.

4   Now scientists have a bigger worry. The Swift-Tuttle comet passed by Earth in 1992. It measured six miles across, the same size as the one that may have wiped out the dinosaurs. It was at a safe distance of 110 million miles. But traveling at 37 miles a second, it's due to return in August of 2126. And then there's a 1-in-10,000 chance that it could strike Earth.

5   Luckily, there's time to get ready for this slight chance. Some scientists want to make plans to launch a rocket. Inside the rocket would be explosives. If the comet *is* on course to hit Earth, a strong explosion might move it away before disaster strikes.

Circle the correct answer for questions 1–5.
Write your answer to question 6 on a separate piece of paper.

1. The asteroid that passed Earth in 1989 was _____ Swift-Tuttle.

    A the same size as

    B much larger than

    C closer to Earth than

    D farther from Earth than

2. Which word in paragraph 1 means "the remains of something broken down"?

    A grain

    B debris

    C pounds

    D mountain

3. Which paragraph tells what might happen in August of 2126?

    A 1

    B 2

    C 3

    D 4

4. What could have resulted from the huge asteroid hitting Earth in 1989?

    A an overabundance of crops

    B more intense sunlight

    C a terrible draught

    D tidal waves

5. You can infer from the article that _____.

    A comets are faster than asteroids

    B scientists can always predict when a comet is on the way

    C if an asteroid hit, the Earth would have a shortage of food

    D even without a comet, the dinosaurs would never have survived

6. Do you think launching a rocket toward the Swift-Tuttle comet is a good idea? Why or why not?

What were the Negro Leagues?

1. Moses Walker became a major-league baseball player in 1884. Walker, a black man, ran into a wall of racism. He was a catcher, and pitchers ignored his signals. Other players refused to take the field against him. Walker was soon out of baseball. He was the last African American to play in the majors until Jackie Robinson in 1947.

2. In the years between, black baseball players played for all-black teams. At first, they were independent teams. They traveled from city to city and set up games with other teams. This was called "barnstorming." But in 1919, a former pitcher, Rube Foster, organized the Negro National League. The team owners, as well as the players, were black.

3. Foster's league was a success until the Great Depression of the 1930s finished it. Later, other Negro leagues were organized. Their games were often played in major-league parks. The yearly Negro All-Star Game would draw 50,000 fans.

4. Many of the players truly were all-stars. They included Oscar Charleston, William "Judy" Johnson, and James "Cool Papa" Bell. Josh Gibson, a hard-hitting catcher, was called "the black Babe Ruth." And Leroy "Satchel" Paige was one of the greatest pitchers who played in any league. Barnstorming black teams would often play teams of white major leaguers. The black teams won 309 of these games and lost 129.

5. The "color barrier" in major-league baseball came to an end in 1947. As more black players entered the major leagues, the Negro leagues began to die. By 1955, they were gone. African Americans had lost something that was theirs. But few would have wanted it any other way. Most would agree with Buck O'Neil, a former Negro league player and major-league coach: "It never should have been, a Negro league. Shouldn't have been."

Circle the correct answer for questions 1–5.
Write your answer to question 6 on a separate piece of paper.

1. The man who organized the Negro National League was _____.

   A Moses Walker

   B Rube Foster

   C Josh Gibson

   D Buck O'Neil

2. Which word in paragraph 2 means "acting on one's own"?

   A barnstorming

   B independent

   C organized

   D former

3. Which paragraph talks about the all-stars of the Negro leagues?

   A 1

   B 2

   C 3

   D 4

4. What brought an end to the Negro National League?

   A Jackie Robinson entered the major leagues.

   B The first Negro All-Star Game was played.

   C Moses Walker stopped playing baseball.

   D The Great Depression began.

5. You can conclude from the article that the Negro Leagues began after Moses Walker and began to die out after _____.

   A Jackie Robinson

   B "Satchel" Paige

   C Rube Foster

   D Buck O'Neil

6. Reread the quote from Buck O'Neil at the end of the article. What do you think he meant? Write an opinion piece either agreeing or disagreeing with his point of view.

How do spinning ice skaters keep from getting dizzy?

1   Ice skaters often look like a blur when they go into a spin that turns their bodies in a full circle several times each second. Just watching them can make a person feel dizzy. Yet when skaters finally stop, they don't fall down or even look dizzy. They have somehow learned to control their dizziness. How do they do it?

2   The answer is in the ears. Deep inside people's ears are three small, curving tubes—the semicircular canals. These canals are filled with a liquid called *endolymph*. Whenever a skater moves, the endolymph sloshes around and excites tiny hairs. The hairs signal the brain that the skater is moving.

3   Skaters feel fine as long as they keep spinning. The problem is that they have to stop spinning sometime. When they stop, the endolymph keeps sloshing around for a while. The message to the brain still says the body is moving. The eyes, though, are telling the brain that the body has stopped. Scientists think these opposite messages are what make a person dizzy.

4   Skaters have a trick that puts an end to dizziness. They quickly toss their head toward the side opposite their spin. To the people watching, it may look as though skaters are shaking the hair out of their eyes, but something important is happening inside the semicircular canals. Receiving a slosh in the opposite side, the endolymph evens out. Another message goes out to the brain: The body has stopped. Because both the eyes and the hairs in the semicircular canals are sending the same message, the dizziness goes away.

Circle the correct answer for questions 1–5.
Write your answer to question 6 on a separate piece of paper.

1. Ice skaters can look like a blur because they _____.
   A get dizzy
   B wear fancy outfits
   C skate at high speeds
   D spin several circles a second

2. Which word in paragraph 2 means "stirs up or makes more active"?
   A excites
   B signal
   C moves
   D tubes

3. Which paragraph tells how skaters keep from getting dizzy?
   A 1
   B 2
   C 3
   D 4

4. What happens when skaters toss their heads to the side opposite their spin?
   A They spin in the opposite direction.
   B The endolymph stops moving.
   C The endolymph evens out.
   D They get dizzier.

5. You can infer from the article that _____.
   A professional skaters avoid spinning while performing
   B professional skaters do not get dizzy while performing
   C skaters have larger ear canals than the average person
   D scientists know exactly what makes a person dizzy

6. Training for anything—like championship skating—takes a great deal of skill, time, and hard work. Describe how you would train for something you wanted to be "best" at. Write your training routine in journal format.

Where did potato chips come from?

1   If it hadn't been for a picky eater and a stubborn cook, one of America's favorite snacks might never have come to be. The story starts with Thomas Jefferson, who became a fan of French fries when he visited Paris in the 1700s. On his return to America, Jefferson served them at his dinner parties. His friends loved the thick, crisp potato strips. They began to cook and serve them in their own homes.

2   Soon French fries were offered in some of the best restaurants in the country, such as Moon Lake Lodge in Saratoga Springs, New York. In 1853, Native American George Crum was the cook at this restaurant. He was proud of his French fries. That is, until he faced a picky eater. The man said his order of French fries was not thin enough and sent it back to the kitchen.

3   Crum was surprised. But wanting to please, he cut some potatoes into thinner strips and fried them. "Still not thin enough," said the picky diner. Now Crum was getting angry. He decided to teach the man a lesson. So he cut up some potatoes as thin as paper. After he fried them, the potato slices were so crisp and thin that they had to be picked up with the fingers. To Crum's amazement, the man loved these potato "chips." Curious diners at nearby tables wanted to try the new dish, too. Soon Crum had to make potato chips every day.

4   The potato chip became even more popular after 1920. In that year, a machine was invented to peel potatoes. Cooks no longer had to do this job by hand, which saved a lot of time. Today, Americans eat more potato chips than people anywhere else in the world.

Reading for Comprehension

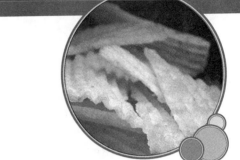

Circle the correct answer for questions 1–5.
Write your answer to question 6 on a separate piece of paper.

1. The article does *not* tell _____.

    A who George Crum was

    B where Moon Lake Lodge was

    C how potato chips became popular

    D when potato chips began to be sold in bags

2. Which word in paragraph 1 means "not willing to change one's mind or way of doing things"?

    A crisp

    B thick

    C favorite

    D stubborn

3. Which paragraph tells how the first potato chip was made?

    A 1

    B 2

    C 3

    D 4

4. What happened after George Crum started serving potato chips?

    A He started serving French fries.

    B Thomas Jefferson visited Paris.

    C A machine was invented to peel potatoes.

    D He began cooking at the Moon Lake Lodge.

5. You can infer from the article that George Crum was _____.

    A a successful cook

    B never a fan of French fries

    C a friend of Thomas Jefferson

    D proud to be a Native American

6. Write one or two paragraphs to describe how you think your favorite snack food is made. After the set of directions, explain what makes the food so appealing to you.

What place on Earth gets the most rain?

1   Rain forests are the habitats of more than half of all plants and animals in the world. There are rain forests in South America, Africa, and Southeast Asia. But where would you suppose is the rainiest rain forest of them all?

2   If you guessed the United States—you're right! Mount Waialeale (wy•AH•lay•AH•lay), Hawaii, is the wettest place on Earth—not counting the oceans, of course. It gets a yearly average of 460 inches of rain. But sometimes 600 inches of rain can fall. In contrast, yearly rainfall in the Amazon rain forest of Brazil is about 200 inches.

3   Mount Waialeale is on the island of Kauai. Its peak, about 5,000 feet above the sea, is always covered in mist. Rivers dropping from the peak have carved deep canyons. They cut through layers of rock formed by the island's volcanoes. The sharp ridges of solid lava are thickly covered with rare plants. They fall away to high red cliffs. Ribbons of waterfalls fall down into deep gorges.

4   Many of Hawaii's native plants and animals live nowhere else on Earth. And many species living on Mount Waialeale are found nowhere else in Hawaii. They are plants with huge, brightly colored flowers that look like an artist's dream. But like many rain forest species, these plants and animals are threatened. Over the years, people have brought new species to Kauai. They compete with native plants for space and light. Goats, pigs, and other animals eat and step on the plants.

5   More than 20 plant species found only on Kauai are considered endangered. The island's bird and insect species also are threatened. There have been efforts to preserve their habitat—the rainiest place on Earth.

Circle the correct answer for questions 1–5.
Write your answer to question 6 on a separate piece of paper.

1. Mount Waialeale is in _____.
   A Southeast Asia
   B Hawaii
   C Africa
   D Brazil

2. Which word in paragraph 4 means "in danger"?
   A new
   B huge
   C native
   D threatened

3. Which paragraph tells how much rain Mount Waialeale gets every year?
   A 1
   B 2
   C 3
   D 4

4. What has *not* contributed to the decline of native plant species on Mount Waialeale?
   A new species brought to the area
   B animals eating the plants
   C less space and light
   D too much rain

5. You can conclude from the article that _____.
   A someday many Hawaiian plant species will be extinct
   B preservation efforts will save most of the plant species
   C the scenery in Hawaii is a lot like the mainland United States
   D the United States doesn't consider Mount Waialeale a rain forest

6. Why would the rainiest place on Earth have plants that are found nowhere else? Why would a threat to these plants also endanger birds and insects?

Who was Georgia O'Keeffe?

1   "But why do you live out here?" a writer once asked the old woman.

2   Georgia O'Keeffe pointed to the bright, barren landscape behind them. "Because this desert is the most beautiful place in the world," she answered. "And because I love my home. I bought my house just for the door. I've made hundreds of paintings of that door."

3   This accomplished artist was born in Wisconsin in 1887. When she was a young girl, her family moved to Virginia. There O'Keeffe began to study art. Even then she had a highly personal style that impressed her teachers. She especially liked to paint simple, everyday things like doors, flowers, houses, the desert hills, and the sun-bleached skulls of dead cattle.

4   In 1916, Georgia O'Keeffe had her first exhibit. Her paintings were an immediate hit. The uncommon beauty and light of her work made this painter famous throughout the world.

5   Until she died in 1986, O'Keeffe made her home in the New Mexico desert. Sadly, toward the end of her long life, the brilliant light faded. O'Keeffe could no longer see to paint her desert world. But today Georgia O'Keeffe's works hang in many of the great museums of the world. And people everywhere can see and feel the beauty of "her" desert.

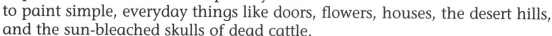
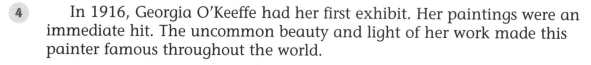

Circle the correct answer for questions 1–5.
Write your answer to question 6 on a separate piece of paper.

1. Georgia O'Keeffe's paintings _____.
   A show city life
   B have never been exhibited
   C resemble those of other artists
   D hang in many great museums

2. Which word in paragraph 2 means "not able to produce growing things," or "empty"?
   A bright
   B barren
   C beautiful
   D paintings

3. Which paragraph tells when Georgia O'Keeffe first exhibited her paintings?
   A 1
   B 2
   C 3
   D 4

4. What happened first in the life of Georgia O'Keeffe?
   A She moved to Virginia.
   B She began to study art.
   C She had her first exhibit.
   D She moved to New Mexico.

5. You can infer from the article that Georgia O'Keeffe's paintings are _____.
   A no longer considered unique
   B worth a lot of money
   C dark and gloomy
   D mostly of people

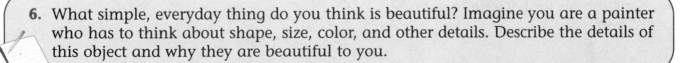

6. What simple, everyday thing do you think is beautiful? Imagine you are a painter who has to think about shape, size, color, and other details. Describe the details of this object and why they are beautiful to you.

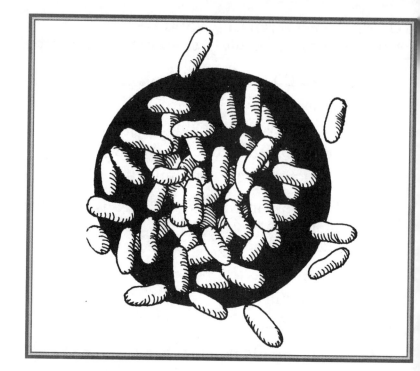

1   Thick oil oozes between rocks. Smelly garbage floats in a stream. Dead plants rot in a garbage bag. The pollution is enough to make you lose your appetite. Yet those messes look pretty tasty to certain kinds of bacteria. If the bacteria get a chance to go to work, they can make most of that waste and pollution harmless and sometimes even helpful.

2   Using bacteria to clean up pollution is called *bioremediation.* One of the first times the method was used was on the *Queen Mary.* The beautiful old ship was brought into a California harbor many years ago. It was to be turned into a hotel, until the fire department put a stop to it. It seems that old oil and tar in the lower part of the ship could have caused a bad fire. It was a perfect dining room for the hungry bacteria, though. In less than six weeks, the ship was clean.

3   Bacteria also have been sent to work under the ground. There they eat up things that pollute our drinking water. They also gobble up gasoline that leaks from storage tanks.

4   Other good bacteria help gardeners. Food scraps and dead plants are put into a pile in a yard and covered with leaves or wood chips. As long as the pile stays wet and the bacteria can "breathe" they will eat up the pile and change it into fertilizer. The gardener puts this fertilizer into the soil, and plants grow bigger and faster.

5   If bacteria work on garden waste, why couldn't they work on big cities' landfills? Well, these landfills often don't have enough air for helpful bacteria's taste. Without air, good bacteria won't eat, and the pollution won't go away. But maybe someday soon landfills will be built that have enough air for bacteria to eat.

Circle the correct answer for questions 1–5.
Write your answer to question 6 on a separate piece of paper.

1. The lower part of the *Queen Mary* was covered with _____.

   A soil

   B leaves

   C salt water

   D oil and tar

2. Which word in paragraph 4 means "material that helps plants grow"?

   A gardeners

   B fertilizer

   C leaves

   D pile

3. Which paragraph tells about a problem with landfills?

   A 1

   B 2

   C 4

   D 5

4. What is the most important factor for bacteria to do its job?

   A air

   B fertilizer

   C moisture

   D oil and tar

5. You can infer from the article that bacteria _____.

   A will solve the world's pollution problems

   B can save gardeners money on fertilizer

   C are only effective above ground

   D never exist in landfills

6. Bacteria can be helpful, but they alone won't save Earth. Write a letter to the editor of your local newspaper to persuade people to change their daily lives to help cut down on pollution and waste.

When was the Internet invented?

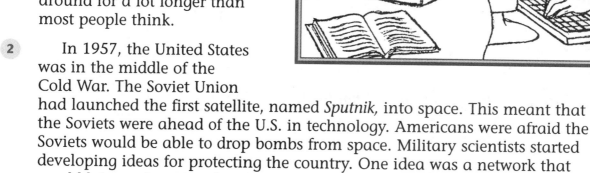

1   Today, people use the Internet to shop, play games, make friends, and read the news. Many young people cannot imagine life without it. Most older people, on the other hand, think the Internet is only 10 or 15 years old. That is really only true of many of its current uses. The Internet has been around for a lot longer than most people think.

2   In 1957, the United States was in the middle of the Cold War. The Soviet Union had launched the first satellite, named *Sputnik,* into space. This meant that the Soviets were ahead of the U.S. in technology. Americans were afraid the Soviets would be able to drop bombs from space. Military scientists started developing ideas for protecting the country. One idea was a network that would let people across the country communicate using computers.

3   This network took a decade to develop. It was first tried out in 1969. For the next two decades it was used solely by scientists who worked with the U.S. government, and by some engineers and librarians. Then, in 1990, the military turned over control of the Internet to the National Science Foundation. The Internet then became available to colleges all over the United States and to scientists throughout Europe.

4   The biggest change in the way that people use the Internet came in 1992. For the first time, access was opened to the general public, creating what is now known as the World Wide Web. Soon, people began finding all kinds of different things they could do with this worldwide network. Today, no one government or company is in charge of the Internet, and it just gets bigger and bigger.

Circle the correct answer for questions 1–5.
Write your answer to question 6 on a separate piece of paper.

1. The Internet was started _____.
   A in 1992
   B in space
   C by the Soviet Union
   D by the U.S. government

2. Which word in paragraph 3 means "only"?
   A first
   B solely
   C control
   D throughout

3. Which paragraph tells why the Internet was started?
   A 1
   B 2
   C 3
   D 4

4. You can infer from the article that _____.
   A the Internet is still controlled by the military
   B the Soviet Union used the Internet to build *Sputnik*
   C people have been able to download music from the Internet since 1969
   D the people who started the Internet didn't know how it would be used today

5. *Current* can have the following meanings. Mark the meaning used in paragraph 1.
   A electrical charge
   B course of events
   C present
   D flow

6. Imagine that the Internet stopped working. Write a journal entry describing how your life would change.

How was the Grand Canyon formed?

1   Every year, millions of people travel from around the world to visit the Grand Canyon. After many miles of desert and forest, they come to a place where the land drops off. Standing at the edges of great cliffs, they see a world of gigantic rock formations climbing thousands of feet from below in all kinds of shapes and colors. It is like nothing else on Earth.

2   For more than 130 years, people have been trying to figure out how this unique place was formed. There are many different theories. The best known explanation is that the Grand Canyon was carved by the Colorado River. For millions of years, this powerful river has run through the Colorado Plateau. It floods in the spring and carries loose desert soil with it, making the canyon deeper and wider.

3   Many scientists discount this theory because they believe that the canyon is older than the river. They think that, in fact, the canyon was carved by older rivers. Many millions of years ago, Arizona contained a lot more water than it does now. This water flowed into ancient rivers. Later, the climate grew more dry. When the Colorado River came pouring down from the Rockies, it found the Grand Canyon a perfect place to run through.

4   Regardless of what river formed the Grand Canyon, today the Colorado River is carving its course through black rocks about 700 million years old. No words or pictures can give people a fair idea of this canyon that is 200 miles long and more than a mile deep. The colorful carvings and magnificent peaks and towers are a beautiful and always changing sight to visitors of this national landmark.

Circle the correct answer for questions 1–5.
Write your answer to question 6 on a separate piece of paper.

1. Tourists travel to the Grand Canyon mainly to see _____.

   A the Colorado River

   B the Colorado Plateau

   C the desert and forest

   D the gigantic rock formations

2. Which word in paragraph 2 means "one of a kind"?

   A best

   B unique

   C different

   D powerful

3. Which paragraph tells what is wrong with the theory that the Colorado River carved the Grand Canyon?

   A 1   C 3

   B 2   D 4

4. The article says that all the following may have helped form the Grand Canyon *except* _____.

   A the Colorado River

   B loose desert soil

   C ancient rivers

   D tornadoes

5. You can infer from the article that _____.

   A it is hard to tell how something so old was formed

   B everyone agrees about how the Grand Canyon was formed

   C people knew how the Grand Canyon was formed 130 years ago

   D the area dried out because all the water poured into the Colorado River

6. Think about a natural landmark near you. Write a short essay suggesting how it might have been formed.

What vehicle helped win a war?

1   The year was 1943, two years after the United States entered World War II. Five American soldiers bumped along the back roads of Italy. They were riding in what the driver called a "beetle bug." The passengers had other names for the rugged little vehicle, such as "Leaping Lena" and "puddle jumper." But one young man gave it the name that stuck. He called the boxy little car a jeep.

2   The Army had asked for a light car about three feet high that could take on rough roads. A list of what they wanted was sent to U.S. automakers. When the first model was made, the Army put it to the test. The little car raced over log roads, plowed through sand traps, and slogged through a huge mud pit. It even climbed stairs. After 3,400 miles of rough driving, the vehicle was still in one piece and running fine. The Army liked what they saw, so they ordered it.

3   By 1945, more than 600,000 jeeps were on the battlefields of World War II. The sturdy little jeep looked rather like a sardine can on wheels. But it took American soldiers over land that drivers of other cars and trucks would never dream of trying. General Dwight Eisenhower said the jeep was one reason the United States won the war.

4   After the war, people still wondered where the jeep got its name. Some people claimed that it came from the initials *G.P.*, which stood for "general purpose." Others, using a bit more imagination, remembered a character named Eugene the Jeep from Popeye cartoons. This cartoon character seemed able to do nearly anything. To those who drove it, that sounded like a good description of the hardworking jeep.

Circle the correct answer for questions 1–5.
Write your answer to question 6 on a separate piece of paper.

1. The article does *not* tell _____.
   A how many jeeps there were in 1945
   B other nicknames for the jeep
   C when World War II ended
   D who Eugene the Jeep was

2. Which word in paragraph 1 means "able to endure a great deal; tough"?
   A little
   B boxy
   C rugged
   D passengers

3. Which paragraph tells how the Army tested the jeep?
   A 1
   B 2
   C 3
   D 4

4. Why was the Army confident enough to order the jeep?
   A General Eisenhower liked it.
   B It was built in the United States.
   C It was tested over many miles of rough driving.
   D It was the only vehicle that was three feet high.

5. You can infer from the article that _____.
   A *G.P.* described things that had many uses
   B jeeps also were used in World War I
   C no one bought jeeps after the war
   D soldiers feared jeeps

6. Where would you *not* want to drive a jeep? Why?

Who was the "African Eve"?

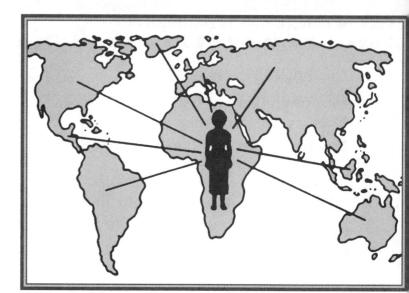

1　　About 200,000 years ago, a certain woman lived in Africa. Historians don't know what her real name was, but all people are part of her family. Every person on Earth is a descendant of the "African Eve."

2　　How is this possible? The answer lies in DNA. DNA is the chemical in living cells that makes every creature unique. It is DNA that makes a horse develop differently than a carrot. It is DNA that causes the differences among people.

3　　Scientists long ago concluded that all modern humans share common ancestors. But when did they live, and where? DNA could help find the answer. Scientists have created a "map" of many human genes. They also know how often some genes *mutate* (MEW•tayt), or change. This information can help them estimate how closely two people are related. But they cannot do this by studying the "ordinary" DNA. That's because half of each person's DNA comes from each parent. Beyond that, you are a scramble of your grandparents and all your ancestors before them.

4　　However, DNA is also found in parts of cells called *mitochondria* (my•toe•KON•dree•uh). This mitochondrial DNA comes from a person's mother only. It can be traced from a woman to her mother to her grandmother, and so on back.

5　　In the 1980s, a group of scientists carefully chose 135 women. They took samples of their mitochondrial DNA. They used a computer to track the differences among them. They found that all human beings shared a common female ancestor about 8,000 generations ago—about 200,000 years. It was almost certain that she lived in Africa.

6　　The "African Eve" is not *the* earliest ancestor of all human beings. But she is our earliest ancestor in the all-female line—the 8,000-times-great grandmother of everyone.

Circle the correct answer for questions 1–5.
Write your answer to question 6 on a separate piece of paper.

1. The chemical in living cells that makes people what they are is called _____.

   A DNA

   B mutate

   C ancestor

   D mitochondria

2. Which word in paragraph 3 means "decided by reasoning"?

   A change

   B created

   C scramble

   D concluded

3. Which paragraph describes how the "African Eve" was discovered?

   A 1

   B 2

   C 3

   D 5

4. Scientists can best estimate how closely two people are related by studying _____.

   A a family tree

   B ordinary DNA

   C mitochondrial DNA

   D the grandparents' genes

5. You can infer from the article that the 135 women chosen for the study _____.

   A all had children

   B all came from Africa

   C were studied in the same lab

   D came from all parts of the world

6. Write a one- or two-paragraph summary of the article you just read.

What is salsa?

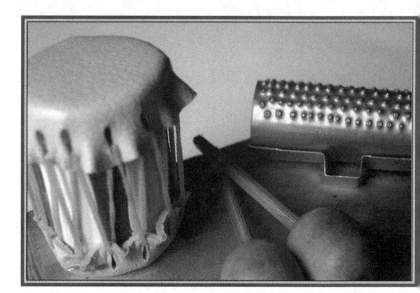

1. People dance around the band shouting, "Salsa!" They want the musicians to add some spice to the song—to make it "hot" like the sauce. That may have been how the music came to be called *salsa.*

2. Salsa probably had its roots in Afro–Cuban music. When the Latin American sound made its way to the United States, those roots mingled with other Latin music and American sounds—jazz, soul, and rock. Some people say salsa is a New York City sound made up by Puerto Rican New Yorkers, sometimes known as "Nuyoricans."

3. One of the keys to the salsa sound is the *clave* (KLAH•vay), the Spanish word for "key." A pair of claves, round wooden sticks, is often played by a salsa band's lead singer. Clave is also the name for the rhythm that makes a piece of salsa music come together.

4. Other instruments are important in salsa, too. The conga drum stands upright and is played with the hands. It comes from the Congolese culture in Africa. A player must stand to play the *timbales,* a steel drum set made up of two drums and a pair of cowbells. Timbales are played with sticks. Bongos, which come from Cuba, are a pair of drums played with the hands. The smaller of the pair is called the *macho* and the larger drum is called the *hembra.*

5. Each instrument adds its sound to those of a piano, bass, two or more horns, and one or two lead singers. The result is hot and spicy—salsa!

Circle the correct answer for questions 1–5.
Write your answer to question 6 on a separate piece of paper.

1. The claves are often played by _____.

   A a pianist

   B a guitarist

   C a drummer

   D a lead singer

2. Which word in paragraph 2 means "mixed, or combined"?

   A roots

   B sound

   C music

   D mingled

3. Which paragraph tells where salsa probably came from?

   A 1

   B 2

   C 3

   D 4

4. Claves are important to the salsa sound because _____.

   A they are played with a string

   B they are played with a cowbell

   C they make a piece of music come together

   D they make the music sound more American

5. You can infer from the article that salsa makes people _____.

   A want to dance

   B want to cry

   C hungry

   D angry

6. What kind of music do you like best? Write a short essay to explain why you like it.

How are fireworks made?

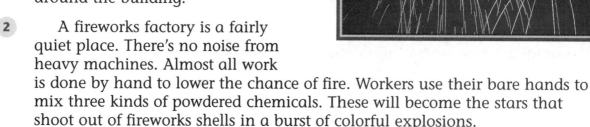

1. Here's the first thing you need to know if you ever visit a fireworks factory: Wear a cotton shirt and pants. This clothing rule is not just for your comfort. Clothes made of materials such as nylon can produce a kind of electricity. Just one spark in a fireworks factory could be explosive. A fire in a Netherlands factory in 2000 resulted in an explosion that leveled a 625-square-yard area around the building.

2. A fireworks factory is a fairly quiet place. There's no noise from heavy machines. Almost all work is done by hand to lower the chance of fire. Workers use their bare hands to mix three kinds of powdered chemicals. These will become the stars that shoot out of fireworks shells in a burst of colorful explosions.

3. In the next step, water is added to the star mix until it looks a bit like mud. Workers can safely pound this "mud" into the shape of a large loaf of bread. It's also safe to cut it into cubes. The star cubes are then coated with gunpowder and set out to dry.

4. Another worker is in charge of putting star cubes into a cardboard shell. Again, this must be done carefully by hand. When the shell is filled, it is put into a hollow steel tube that has gunpowder in the bottom. Three different fuses are needed: one to start, one to make the firework take off into the air, and one to make the firework explode.

5. Fireworks must be handled even more carefully after they leave the factory. The safest way to enjoy a fireworks show is to leave it to the professionals. More than 10,000 people in the United States are hurt each year when they use fireworks in their own backyard shows.

Circle the correct answer for questions 1–5.
Write your answer to question 6 on a separate piece of paper.

1. Fireworks factories do *not* have _____.

    A powdered chemicals

    B safety regulations

    C cardboard shells

    D heavy machines

2. Which word in paragraph 4 means "cords that are lighted to set off charges"?

    A tube

    B shell

    C fuses

    D cubes

3. Which paragraph tells what you should wear in a fireworks factory?

    A 1

    B 2

    C 3

    D 4

4. What happens after water is added to the star mix when making fireworks?

    A Star cubes are coated with gunpowder.

    B A cardboard shell is filled with star cubes.

    C Workers mix three kinds of powdered chemicals.

    D The "mud" is pounded into the shape of a loaf of bread.

5. You can conclude from the article that _____.

    A most people who work in fireworks factories take great care in their work

    B most people who work in fireworks factories wear nylon uniforms

    C workers wear bulky protective gloves in the factory

    D workers never touch fireworks outside the factory

6. Describe the best fireworks show you've ever seen. What made it unique?

Who was Sequoya?

1   Sequoya paced nervously in front of the council house. Inside, the Cherokee chiefs were testing his daughter. They ordered the girl to write down everything they said, exactly as they said it. Then Sequoya would try to read what she had written. If he failed, the most important work of his life would be rejected.

2   The year was 1821. Up until then, none of the 25,000 members of the Cherokee tribe had been able to read or write. The reason was simple. There was no alphabet to represent their spoken language.

3   Young Sequoya had seen white soldiers reading "talking leaves." Though their families were far away, the white men could "talk" to them through letters. Sequoya wanted the Cherokees to be able to write their language. For 12 years, he worked on a Cherokee alphabet. Then he taught it to his daughter. Now he was about to find out if the Cherokee tribe would accept his invention.

4   Finally the door to the council house opened. Sequoya went inside. Holding the paper his daughter had written on, he read her words without a mistake. The chiefs were amazed! For the first time, the Cherokee language could be written down and understood.

5   Sequoya received many honors for his outstanding invention. But the most fitting monuments to the great Cherokee scholar are the giant sequoia trees of California, which bear his name.

Circle the correct answer for questions 1–5.
Write your answer to question 6 on a separate piece of paper.

1. The article does *not* tell how _____ the Cherokee alphabet.
   A many letters are in
   B Sequoya got the idea for
   C the Cherokee chiefs felt about
   D Sequoya and his daughter were tested on

2. Which word in paragraph 5 means "someone with a lot of knowledge about a subject"?
   A monuments
   B scholar
   C honors
   D giant

3. Which paragraph tells how long Sequoya worked on the Cherokee alphabet?
   A 1
   B 2
   C 3
   D 4

4. What happened after Sequoya read to the Cherokee council?
   A The chiefs tested his daughter.
   B White soldiers read "talking leaves."
   C He taught the alphabet to his daughter.
   D Trees in California were named for him.

5. *Ordered* can have the following meanings. Mark the meaning used in paragraph 1.
   A sent for
   B arranged
   C commanded
   D marked by discipline

6. Write a short essay to explain why a language needs a system for writing. Use examples from the article to support your argument.

What is it like to be inside an erupting volcano?

1   Early in 1993, scientists climbed into the cone of the Galeras Volcano in Colombia. They wanted to test new ways to find out when a volcano might erupt and put people's lives in danger. Suddenly, the volcano began to rumble. With a terrible roar, red-hot rocks, lava, and ash shot miles into the sky. Six of the scientists, as well as three tourists exploring nearby, were killed.

2   Dr. Stanley Williams, one of the scientists, was lucky. He had been standing near the edge of the volcano, getting ready to leave. When rocks as big as television sets began falling, Williams turned and ran as fast as he could. He didn't make it very far, though. Debris from the eruption broke both his legs and injured his head. Seeking a safe place behind some large rocks, he tried to stay conscious as the ground shook and thundered around him. He knew he needed to stay awake because there would be another blast. When it came an hour later, he watched for falling rocks and dodged out of their path.

3   Two hours after the first explosion, Williams heard voices. He looked up and saw two women carrying a stretcher down the slope into the crater. They lifted Williams out, and a helicopter flew him to a hospital.

4   Williams recovered from his injuries and continues to study volcanoes. But he is trying to make his job safer. With new technology, Williams can observe a volcano from a safe distance and still find out most of what he wants to learn. Now he can continue to save others' lives as well as his own.

Circle the correct answer for questions 1–5.
Write your answer to question 6 on a separate piece of paper.

1. The Galeras Volcano is in _____.
   A Alaska
   B Mexico
   C Colombia
   D Venezuela

2. Which word in paragraph 2 means "able to see, feel, hear, and know what is happening"?
   A broke
   B shook
   C dodged
   D conscious

3. Which paragraph tells how Dr. Williams was rescued?
   A 1
   B 2
   C 3
   D 4

4. Why did Dr. Williams need to stay awake after the first eruption?
   A so he could react to another blast
   B so he could save the lives of tourists
   C so he could look for the rescue team
   D so he could study what the volcano was doing

5. You can infer from the article that _____.
   A Dr. Williams is afraid of volcanoes
   B it is impossible to predict eruptions
   C studying volcanoes is more dangerous now than ever
   D people who study volcanoes are willing to risk their lives for their work

6. Would you be willing to do work that is considered dangerous? Why or why not?

What useful invention was almost too late?

1   The British soldier was hungry. He eyed the tin can. His dinner was inside, but he couldn't get at it. The Englishman first tried to open the can with his pocketknife. That didn't work. Then he attacked it with his bayonet, but all he got was a cut thumb. By this time, the soldier was angry. He set the can on a tree stump and fired away. And that's how most tin cans were opened during the War of 1812.

2   The tin cannister was invented in Britain in 1810. Sir William Parry took along canned meat when he went to explore the Arctic in 1824. Even though the tin can kept Parry's food fresh, the explorer probably wasn't too happy with it. The directions on the can read "Cut round the top with a chisel and hammer." Besides, even an empty can weighed more than a pound.

3   It wasn't until 1861, the start of the Civil War, that people in the United States began using the tin can. Preserved food was needed for soldiers of both the North and South. By this time, too, a kind of can opener had been invented. It had a sharp, curved blade that had to be forced into the edge of the can. Still, working the opener around the top of the can was no easy job. It could be dangerous as well.

4   Finally, in 1870, an American invented a can opener that looked much like the one in kitchens today. Its cutting wheel rolled around the edge of the can. Years later, another American changed the can opener a bit. Now the can circled around the cutting wheel. Billions of cans later, the can opener— or its electric version—is still an important kitchen tool.

Circle the correct answer for questions 1–5.
Write your answer to question 6 on a separate piece of paper.

1. A modern can opener was invented in _____.

   A 1810

   B 1824

   C 1861

   D 1870

2. Which word in paragraph 2 means "a tool used to cut or shape wood, stone, or metal"?

   A chisel

   B pound

   C explorer

   D hammer

3. Which paragraph tells where the tin can was invented?

   A 1

   B 2

   C 3

   D 4

4. What led to the tin can being used in the United States?

   A the end of the Civil War

   B the invention of the can opener

   C Sir William Parry's Arctic expedition

   D the need for preserved food for soldiers

5. *Fresh* can have the following meanings. Mark the meaning used in paragraph 2.

   A pure, or not spoiled

   B new or different

   C not salty

   D rude

6. There is an old saying, "Necessity is the mother of invention." How does it apply to the can opener?

How can you make your own paper?

1.   Here's a way to turn old newspaper into new paper. First, you'll need to gather these things: newspaper, a bucket, a cooking pan, dishwashing liquid, a sieve, an electric blender, a large bowl, a spoon, an eight-inch square of wire screen, old towels, and two bricks.

2.   To start, tear eight pages of newspaper into strips, put them in the bucket, and cover them with water. After they soak for a few hours, pour off the extra water. Put the paper in the cooking pan. Add one tablespoon of dishwashing liquid and cover the paper with water. Cook the paper mixture on very low heat for two hours. Add water to keep the paper covered if you need to. The paper should turn into a pulp.

3.   Let the mixture cool, then drain it in the sieve. Put the paper pulp, a handful at a time, into the electric blender. Add water so the blender is three-fourths full. Turn it on for a few seconds, then turn it off. Repeat for one minute. Dump the pulp into the large bowl and stir in more water.

4.   After all the pulp has been blended, slide the screen into the bowl and get a thin, even covering of pulp on it. Put the screen, pulp side down, on an old towel and press down hard. Lift the screen, leaving the pulp behind. Put another old towel on top of the pulp and press down.

5.   Repeat with other layers of pulp and towels. Put the bricks on top of the pile and leave it for one day. Then peel off the pieces of paper you've made and let them dry on newspaper. After your new pieces of paper are dry, you can cut them in any shape you want and put them to use.

Circle the correct answer for questions 1–5.
Write your answer to question 6 on a separate piece of paper.

1. The article does *not* tell _____.

   A how long to soak the newspaper

   B what color the finished paper is

   C what materials are needed

   D how to make the pulp flat

2. Which word in paragraph 2 means "ground-up wood or rags mixed with water, used to make paper"?

   A pulp

   B strips

   C liquid

   D pages

3. Which paragraph tells how to dry the paper?

   A 2

   B 3

   C 4

   D 5

4. When making paper, what should a person do before draining the pulp mixture in the sieve?

   A let the mixture cool

   B put a screen over the mixture

   C dump the mixture into a bowl

   D put the mixture into a blender

5. You can infer from the article that when making paper it is important to _____.

   A use a new blender

   B press and dry the pulp

   C work with a team of people

   D cook the paper mixture as fast as possible

6. Using the format of the article, write directions for how to make something.

Who is Ellen Ochoa?

1   Ellen Ochoa was 11 years old in 1969 when the first man walked on the moon. At the time, she did not imagine that she would ever be an astronaut. She was female, and she was Hispanic. Those were two things that made her different from any of the space travelers at the time. Little did she imagine then that she would help to change that. Years later she would become the first Hispanic female astronaut.

2   The first woman to become an astronaut was Sally Ride. That was in 1983. At the time, Ochoa was in graduate school. She was studying to be an engineer. After receiving her Ph.D. in 1985, she decided to follow in Sally Ride's footsteps. She got a job with a company that worked with the National Aeronautics and Space Administration (NASA).

3   At first, her work was in a laboratory, not outer space. There, she designed computer systems and worked with optics. The word *optics* refers to devices used for seeing. Ochoa helped to invent a number of optical devices, including a system that uses robots to build things.

4   The people at NASA were impressed with Ochoa's work. In 1990, they accepted her into the astronaut training program. A year later, she became an official U.S. astronaut. Since then she has gone on a number of space shuttle missions. On the shuttle, she has studied the sun's effects on the Earth's climate and the damage that has been done to the ozone layer. In her work on Earth and in space, Ellen Ochoa has inspired many people to follow their dreams, whatever their gender or race.

Circle the correct answer for questions 1–5.
Write your answer to question 6 on a separate piece of paper.

1. Ellen Ochoa was the first _____ to become an astronaut.
   A woman
   B engineer
   C Hispanic female
   D NASA employee

2. Which word in paragraph 4 means "motivated"?
   A inspired
   B training
   C accepted
   D impressed

3. Which paragraph tells what made Ellen Ochoa decide to become an astronaut?
   A 1
   B 2
   C 3
   D 4

4. Ellen Ochoa's story shows that if you want to be an astronaut it is a good idea to _____.
   A watch a lot of science fiction movies
   B play a lot of video games
   C get a good education
   D join the military

5. You can infer from the article that _____.
   A Ellen Ochoa became an astronaut because she is Hispanic
   B Sally Ride was a role model for Ellen Ochoa
   C Ellen Ochoa has been to the moon
   D becoming an astronaut is easy

6. Write a short essay to explain what aspects of Ellen Ochoa's life make her a good role model.

1   Wolves were the first thing the man thought of. He was by himself in northern Minnesota when his car broke down. It is one of only two states with a large number of wolves. The man could have walked to a warm, safe place. But night was falling and he was afraid. He pictured a pack of snarling wolves tearing him apart if he left his car. All night, he stayed in the car shivering with cold and fright.

2   The man need not have worried, though. Wolves attacking human beings is one of the myths that have given the animal such a bad reputation through the years. Wolves kill only for food. Like all wild animals, they fear and run from anything new or strange. Wolves are very smart. They communicate and cooperate with each other in hunting and in caring for their pups.

3   Early hunters greatly admired wolves. They, too, cooperated to find food. But when people began farming, wolves became a threat. They killed sheep and cattle that had replaced the land's wild game. Stories were told about the "big, bad wolf." The wolf's reputation grew worse. For hundreds of years, wolves have been hunted until there are almost none left.

4   In the 1990s, some wolves were brought to the United States to live in Yellowstone National Park. Because of the wolves' bad reputation, farmers and others who lived near these "new" wolves were nervous. They feared that wolves would hurt them or their animals. They tried to get the wolves taken away. In 2000, the case went before a judge, and he ruled that the wolves could stay. Maybe after living near wolves, more people will understand this beautiful, caring animal and help to save it.

Circle the correct answer for questions 1–5.
Write your answer to question 6 on a separate piece of paper.

1. The article does *not* tell _____.
   A why wolves are good hunters
   B why wolves have a bad reputation
   C the park where wolves were brought to live
   D the other state with a large number of wolves

2. Which word in paragraph 2 means "people's opinion of something"?
   A reputation
   B human
   C animal
   D fear

3. Which paragraph tells why wolves are smart?
   A 1
   B 2
   C 3
   D 4

4. Why did wolves become a threat?
   A They were brought to Yellowstone Park.
   B They attacked people in broken-down cars.
   C They killed farm animals that replaced wild game.
   D They communicated with each other when hunting.

5. You can infer from the article that _____.
   A wolves are rare today
   B wolves have become friendlier
   C wolves are hunted for their fur
   D wolves spend a lot of time alone

6. Think of another animal that is misunderstood because of a bad reputation that is not based on fact. Explain why the animal is misunderstood and suggest how people *should* view this animal.

Who was the "underground man"?

1   Digging was hard work under the blistering California sun. The man stopped to wipe the sweat from his face. Then he drove his spade into the ground once more. A few feet down, the spade would go no farther. The man had hit hardpan, a hard layer of subsoil like bare rock. He tossed his spade away in disgust.

2   Baldasare Forestiere had just bought land near Fresno. He wanted to plant an orchard. But the hardpan meant that trees could not take root. Hot and unhappy, Forestiere stared at his land. Then he remembered it was cool underground. Forestiere had worked below the ground on the subway systems in New York City and Boston. Below the hardpan, he knew, the soil would be softer. He began digging again. By the end of the week, he had a large underground room.

3   But Forestiere didn't stop. He kept on digging. Over the next 40 years, the underground man dug a network of nearly 100 rooms, courtyards, and gardens. He planted fruit trees in large tubs and added windows for air and light.

4   Forestiere died many years ago, but his work remains. Today, the Forestiere Gardens are open to the public. Each year thousands of people visit the beautiful underground world that Baldasare Forestiere dug out of the rock.

Circle the correct answer for questions 1–5.
Write your answer to question 6 on a separate piece of paper.

1. The article does *not* tell _____.
   A where Baldasare Forestiere bought land
   B why Baldasare Forestiere bought the land
   C how many rooms Baldasare Forestiere dug
   D whether Baldasare Forestiere lived underground

2. Which word in paragraph 3 means "system of connecting parts"?
   A underground
   B courtyards
   C network
   D gardens

3. Which paragraph tells where Baldasare Forestiere worked before he moved to California?
   A 1
   B 2
   C 3
   D 4

4. What happened last in the article?
   A Baldasare Forestiere bought land near Fresno.
   B Baldasare Forestiere worked on subway systems.
   C Baldasare Forestiere planted underground gardens.
   D Baldasare Forestiere dug his first underground room.

5. You can infer from the article that _____.
   A fruit trees need hardpan to grow
   B fruit trees won't grow in underground tubs
   C Baldasare Forestiere was a determined man
   D Baldasare Forestiere didn't like working in the subways

6. The land Baldasare Forestiere bought wasn't suited to what he had in mind. What else do you think he could have done with his land? Why do you think so?

How can a plant invade a country?

1   Movies have terrified viewers by showing strange beings invading Earth. In some movies, weird plants have taken over people's bodies. Of course, these movies are fiction. The horrible truth, though, is that alien plants are invading the United States right now!

2   Fortunately, these plants are not going to cause you harm. However, that does not mean that these invasive species aren't causing other problems. An invasive species is one that is not native to a particular area. Of course, some new plants can be harmless and might even appear to be a good addition. For instance, a new type of flower might make a meadow more colorful. On the other hand, if that flower grows on a poisonous plant, animals who don't know that it is not good to eat may die.

3   A more common problem is that these plants take over an area, pushing native plants out. One such plant is called *kudzu*. Kudzu is a vine that is native to Japan. After it was brought to the United States in 1876, many Americans decided that they wanted the green, leafy vine for their gardens. Then, in the 1930s and 1940s, it was used for erosion control. Like other climbing vines, kudzu is good for holding dirt in place.

4   The trouble was that kudzu turned out to fit a bit too well with the climate of the southeastern United States. Before long, it started to show up where people did not want it. Because it grows very fast it is also hard to control. Today kudzu covers huge areas of the South. In some places, people say that they have to close their windows at night to keep kudzu from climbing into their homes.

Circle the correct answer for questions 1–5.
Write your answer to question 6 on a separate piece of paper.

1. The article says that kudzu is _____.
   A poisonous
   B difficult to control
   C from another planet
   D a big problem in Japan

2. Which word in paragraph 1 means "scared"?
   A terrified
   B horrible
   C strange
   D weird

3. Which paragraph tells how kudzu can be useful?
   A 1
   B 2
   C 3
   D 4

4. What has kudzu *not* been used for?
   A garden decoration
   B erosion control
   C seasoning food
   D holding dirt

5. You can infer from the article that _____.
   A non-native plants are useless
   B kudzu sprouts colorful flowers
   C kudzu has been eliminated in Japan
   D people should be careful about introducing new plants

6. Write a one- or two-paragraph summary of the article you just read.

What is an urban legend?

1. A gang is stealing human kidneys. A man is kidnapped and drugged. He wakes up in a tub full of ice. One of his kidneys has been removed.

2. A girl in 1962 had her hair styled in a then-popular "beehive" cut. To keep her hair piled up on top of her head, she didn't wash it for weeks. Bugs nested in her hair and drove her crazy.

3. In the movie *The Wizard of Oz,* there is a quick shot of a man hanging himself.

4. Giant alligators live in the sewers of New York City.

5. All of these stories have one thing in common: They aren't true. They are *urban legends.* An urban legend is a story that appears out of nowhere and is spread by people repeating it as if it were true. It usually is partly funny and partly scary. The scariness is often presented as a warning—for example, to wash one's hair often.

6. Some urban legends are based on fact. For example, in *The Wizard of Oz* you may catch a glimpse of a stagehand ducking behind some scenery. He was caught on the set when the camera started rolling. But most urban legends are based on nothing at all. They take on a life of their own because they make good stories.

7. Take the one about the gang that drove around at night with their car headlights off. When anyone flashed their lights as a friendly warning, the gang would follow the driver and kill him. In 1994, police across the country advised people there was no truth to this story. Four years later, it was still popping up on the Internet.

Circle the correct answer for questions 1–5.
Write your answer to question 6 on a separate piece of paper.

1. One popular urban legend concerns giant _____ in the sewers of New York City.

   A dinosaurs

   B alligators

   C toads

   D rats

2. Which word in paragraph 6 means "quick look"?

   A stagehand

   B glimpse

   C camera

   D scenery

3. Which paragraph tells how urban legends are spread?

   A 1

   B 2

   C 5

   D 6

4. You can infer from the article that most urban legends _____.

   A are based on fact

   B are spread over the radio

   C are based on nothing true

   D are likely to happen in the future

5. *Caught* can have the following meanings. Mark the one used in paragraph 6.

   A discovered by surprise

   B seized or captured

   C stopped oneself

   D entangled

6. Write your own urban legend, remembering that these stories can be both funny and scary.

Are termites helpful or harmful?

1   Returning home from a long trip, the woman dropped her bags at the door. She started across the hardwood floor to open the windows. Two steps later, her foot crashed through the boards! A closer look showed termites chewing away below. Another time, a young boy sat down to play the piano. Suddenly, one of its legs fell off. Thousands of tiny, colorless, antlike creatures scurried out. Termites don't always signal their presence with loud crashes like these. Yet their powerful jaws will destroy anything made of wood.

2   Termites may also add to the warming of Earth. Scientists say that a nest of termites can eat enough wood to give off more than four quarts of methane each minute. Methane and other gases trap heat from the sun and raise temperatures on Earth. If the planet's climate changes, termites could be partly to blame.

3   These little creatures aren't all bad, though. They are an important part of the balance of nature in a forest. Dining on a fallen tree, termites break down the minerals in the tree and return them to the soil. Those minerals then feed other growing plants.

4   Termites not only feed the soil, they also feed animals. You probably know termites can be bird food, but sometimes they are people food! In some parts of the world, the little bugs are a real treat. People who eat them say that termites taste a bit like pineapples. They're good for people, too. A dish of toasted termites is a great source of protein, which people need to live and grow. If termites ever catch on as a food, there will certainly be enough of them to go around. Scientists say that for every person on Earth, there are about 1,000 pounds of termites!

Circle the correct answer for questions 1–5.
Write your answer to question 6 on a separate piece of paper.

1. Termites taste a bit like _____.

   A ants

   B apples

   C chicken

   D pineapples

2. Which word in paragraph 1 means "the fact of being in a particular place"?

   A floor

   B piano

   C presence

   D hardwood

3. Which paragraph tells about termites' place in the balance of nature?

   A 1

   B 2

   C 3

   D 4

4. After termites dine on a fallen tree, _____.

   A they then feed on growing plants

   B minerals are returned to the soil

   C the tree forms new roots

   D they die within 24 hours

5. *Treat* can have the following meanings. Mark the meaning used in paragraph 4.

   A special pleasure

   B pay for someone else

   C handle in a certain way

   D subject to a chemical process

6. Describe another creature that is both helpful and harmful. How is it similar to and different from the termite?

What did Josephine Cochrane invent?

1. Josephine Cochrane didn't wash her dishes. She didn't have to. She was rich enough to have servants to do the job. The problem was, they kept messing it up. Cochrane had expensive china plates in her home in Shelbyville, Illinois. Thanks to the clumsy "help," the collection was being broken piece by piece.

2. This was in the 1880s. It was a great age for new things. Alexander Graham Bell had just invented the telephone, and Thomas Edison invented the light bulb. But no one had invented a machine to wash dishes. Josephine Cochrane set about to build one herself.

3. The inventive woman made wire slots for plates, cups, and saucers. They fit around a wheel set in a copper boiler. As a motor turned the wheel, hot, soapy water squirted over the dishes.

4. Cochrane built a few machines and sold them to her friends. Soon she was getting orders from hotels and restaurants. In 1893, her machine won a top prize at the World's Fair in Chicago.

5. Josephine Cochrane formed a company to make her invention. It was a big success in the hotel and restaurant businesses. In 1914, Cochrane came out with a smaller machine for home kitchens. It was not a success. American housewives, it seemed, didn't mind doing dishes by hand. Also, Cochrane's machine used too much hot water. That made it expensive to use.

6. Josephine Cochrane died a rich woman. But it was not until the 1950s that her invention caught on in American homes.

Circle the correct answer for questions 1–5.
Write your answer to question 6 on a separate piece of paper.

1. Josephine Cochrane invented the automatic dishwasher in _____.
   A the 1950s
   B 1914
   C the 1880s
   D 1893

2. Which word in paragraph 3 means "forced out liquid in a thin stream"?
   A fit
   B made
   C turned
   D squirted

3. Which paragraph tells why Josephine Cochrane invented her machine?
   A 1
   B 2
   C 3
   D 5

4. The smaller version of the dishwashing machine did not catch on right away mainly because _____.
   A people didn't mind doing dishes by hand
   B people couldn't figure out how to use it
   C it was expensive to buy
   D it was too large

5. You can infer from the article that _____.
   A no one uses a dishwashing machine today
   B Josephine Cochrane was a very smart woman
   C dishwashing machines still use too much hot water
   D the dishwashing machine broke the rest of Josephine Cochrane's dishes

6. Why do you think Josephine Cochrane's invention caught on in American homes in the 1950s? What had happened since the early 1900s to cause this change?

Reading for Comprehension 61

When can elephants be backyard pets?

1. Very few of the Rothschild's mynah birds are left in the world. There are under 100 left in the wild. But one of these beautiful white birds shares the home of a woman in Baltimore, Ohio. She is among hundreds of caring people in the United States who are part of the Fish and Wildlife Service's Captive-Bred Wildlife Registration program. Some other endangered animals in the program are Indian elephants, Indian pythons, Himalayan snow leopards, and Grevy's zebras.

2. The program grew out of the Endangered Species Act, passed by Congress in 1973. The Fish and Wildlife Service wanted to save animals that might die out. So it now lets qualified people buy endangered animals and keep them in their homes. Lots of space or even a backyard is not always necessary. Some animals, such as birds and snakes, can live happily in a basement or spare room.

3. Giving a home to endangered animals is not easy. It's a very costly hobby as well. For example, an Indian elephant sells for hundreds of thousands of dollars. Feeding it takes many trips to the grocery store or garden. The animal eats about 100 pounds of hay, grain, fruits, and vegetables each day. Also, cleaning up after elephants or zebras obviously takes more time and effort than cleaning a fish tank or cat box!

4. When endangered animal pets breed and have babies, some are set free into their native settings. This does not always work, though. An animal raised at home might not be able to survive in the wild. It might not know how to find food or recognize natural enemies. But that's not the biggest problem. Such an animal, raised to trust people, can be easy prey for a hunter.

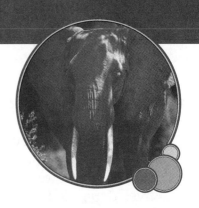

Circle the correct answer for questions 1–5.
Write your answer to question 6 on a separate piece of paper.

1. In 1973, Congress passed an act to help _____.

   A gardens

   B hunters

   C Baltimore, Ohio

   D endangered species

2. Which word in paragraph 2 means "having complied with requirements"?

   A endangered

   B qualified

   C grew

   D spare

3. Which paragraph tells how the Captive-Bred Wildlife Registration program came about?

   A 1

   B 2

   C 3

   D 4

4. What makes caring for some endangered animals such a costly hobby?

   A the amount of food needed

   B cleaning up after the animal

   C hiring experienced animal handlers

   D membership fees in the wildlife program

5. You can infer from the article that _____.

   A anyone can be a part of this program

   B captive animals have no way to breed

   C captive animals always attack their keepers

   D some captive animals need more space than others

6. Explain the kind of requirements someone would need to be a part of the Fish and Wildlife Service's Captive-Bred Wildlife Registration program.

What is Lascaux Cave?

1   Long before people could write, hunters sat around a fire in a cave in the south of France. The day's hunt had gone poorly, and the men were worried. Their lives depended on wildlife. From animals came meat for food, fur and skins for clothing, and fat to burn for light.

2   A hunter walked to the back of the cave. Using a stone knife, he chipped the outline of a galloping deer on the wall. Then he stuck a feather into a small bone and dipped this "brush" into a mixture of charcoal and fat. He traced the deer's shape with the dark paint. Next he partly filled a hollow bone with red paint made from clay. With the end of the bone in his mouth, he blew color onto the drawing. How real the animal looked! The hunter added a final touch—an arrow entering the deer's heart. Surely tomorrow's hunt would succeed now. Such strong magic could not fail.

3   Thousands of years passed. Because of erosion, the wearing away and movement of rock and soil, the cave entrance became tightly sealed. Then, in 1940, four boys were playing nearby. By chance they found a deep hole and hurried to explore it. They dropped 50 feet onto the floor of a cave. The children gasped in wonder. Bulls, horses, reindeer, bears, and even a rhinoceros looked down on them from the cave walls and ceiling.

4   Scientists have studied the Lascaux Cave paintings for many years. They have been found to be more than 17,000 years old. Lascaux Cave is closed to visitors now so that the paintings won't be disturbed. But an exact copy of the cave has been built close by so that the cave artists of the distant past can still speak to the people of today.

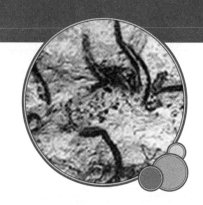

Circle the correct answer for questions 1–5.
Write your answer to question 6 on a separate piece of paper.

1. The article does *not* tell _____.
   A how Lascaux Cave got its name
   B when Lascaux Cave was found
   C who discovered Lascaux Cave
   D where Lascaux Cave is

2. Which word in paragraph 2 means "black material made by heating wood"?
   A charcoal
   B mixture
   C outline
   D hollow

3. Which paragraph tells how the cave artist made his painting?
   A 1
   B 2
   C 3
   D 4

4. In the story of the hunter, what happened before he chipped the outline of a deer?
   A He drew an arrow entering the deer's heart.
   B He traced the deer's shape with dark paint.
   C He blew color onto the drawing.
   D He had a bad day hunting.

5. You can infer from the article that _____.
   A all cave art is red
   B people 17,000 years ago were not spiritual
   C rhinoceroses lived in France 17,000 years ago
   D the copy of Lascaux Cave is better than the cave itself

6. Imagine you were a hunter 17,000 years ago. Write a journal entry that describes what your daily life would be like.

How can 1,000 pets fit into a city apartment?

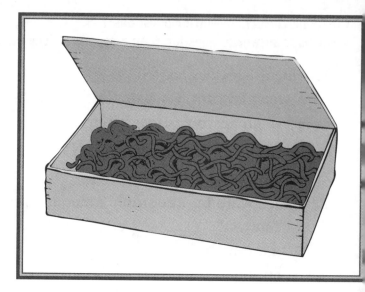

1   The perfect pet for city dwellers needs no leash, litter box, or pet food. This small, quiet, and useful pet is a wiggly worm. It lives in a special box, where it dines on orange peels, coffee grounds, egg shells, and other kitchen leftovers. A worm can eat garbage equal to its own weight in one day. While it turns leftovers into rich soil for gardens or pots on window sills, it also saves space in landfills.

2   A wooden worm box can either be bought or built at home. It should measure about two feet wide and three feet long. It should also have a few small holes in the bottom to let air circulate. Into the box go about four pounds of dampened, shredded newspaper. Then a pound of worms, about 1,000 of them, can move into their new home. Because the worms don't like light, they burrow down into the newspaper. As a final step, the garbage goes in and the cover goes down. Any kind of food garbage—except meat, bones, and greasy food—is fine. The worms will soon go to work to eat up to four pounds of leftovers a week.

3   Not just any kind of worm is suited to a worm box. Earthworms like cool soil, so they should stay outside to do their work. Red worms, though, like warmer places, such as a kitchen or basement, where the temperature stays between 55°F and 77°F. Search for "worms" in the Yellow Pages or on the World Wide Web for places where you can buy this squirmy pet.

Circle the correct answer for questions 1–5.
Write your answer to question 6 on a separate piece of paper.

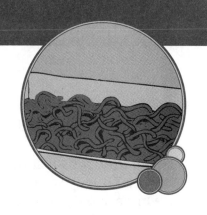

1. The article does *not* tell _____.
   A   what the worms eat
   B   how long the worms live
   C   how big a worm box should be
   D   where earthworms need to live

2. Which word in paragraph 2 means "to move or send around"?
   A   burrow
   B   circulate
   C   measure
   D   work

3. Why aren't earthworms well suited for a worm box?
   A   They like cool soil.
   B   They don't eat garbage.
   C   They don't like to be covered.
   D   They're more expensive than red worms.

4. What is the main idea of the article?
   A   Worms save space in landfills.
   B   Worms are an ideal pet for city dwellers.
   C   Worms can eat up to four pounds of leftovers a week.
   D   Red worms are more appropriate pets than earthworms.

5. You can infer from the article that worm boxes _____.
   A   are also a nice hobby for people outside the city
   B   should be put in the sunniest room of the house
   C   are a good place to toss raw meat
   D   can only be found in a pet store

6. Would you like to have worms as pets? Why or why not?

1.   To the people living in New York City during the 18th century, the six acres of land were not worth much. The land was just outside the city's walls. It wasn't good enough to farm. On very old maps, this area was named "Negros Burial Ground." The bodies of thousands of African Americans, both slave and free, were buried there.

2.   Through the 19th and 20th centuries, New York City grew tremendously. The burial ground was forgotten. The piece of land that was once beyond the city became part of the city center. Both Wall Street, the financial capital of the world, and the ports were nearby. Now the land was worth a lot. In 1990, the United States government wanted to put an office building on the site. Fortunately, the digging couldn't begin right away. By law, the land first had to be explored to see if it was important historically.

3.   Twenty-five feet underground, archaeologists found what could be one of the most important sites in African American history. The bones of 435 people were found. Some were probably the first Africans to be brought to America in the early 1700s. The archaeologists also found an African burial shroud, military buttons, bits of pottery, and what seemed to be the remains of funeral flowers. All the bodies were buried with their heads to the west. The Africans believed the bodies would sit up to face the rising sun on a future Judgment Day.

4.   In 1993, the burial ground was declared a historic landmark. Millions of dollars have gone into studying the site and the people who were found there. The excavated remains will be reburied in New York City upon completion of the research, and an interpretive center and memorial are planned to honor those buried.

Circle the correct answer for questions 1–5.
Write your answer to question 6 on a separate piece of paper.

1. The burial ground was originally _____.

   A just outside the city walls

   B just inside the city walls

   C in the city center

   D on Wall Street

2. Which word in paragraph 3 means "sheet in which dead bodies are wrapped for burying"?

   A military

   B pottery

   C shroud

   D funeral

3. Which paragraph tells what the archaeologists found?

   A 1

   B 2

   C 3

   D 4

4. What happened before the United States government wanted to put an office building on the site of the burial ground?

   A The bones of 435 people were found.

   B The piece of land became part of the city center.

   C The burial ground was declared a historic landmark.

   D New York City studied the site and the people found there.

5. You can conclude from the article that the burial ground _____.

   A also contained the remains of European settlers

   B now has office buildings on the site

   C has been used for farming

   D is still being studied

6. Write a short essay to explain what you would you like to learn from a discovery such as the African American burial ground.

1   Pinned to the classroom bulletin board are three photographs. The first shows teenagers playing volleyball on a beach. In the second picture, two girls lean from an old boat to fill a bottle with murky water from a shallow lake. Sweating in the hot sun, the boy in the third picture digs into hard soil. These three pictures have something in common. They show how high school students spent their summer vacation. The beach picture shows what many teenagers do during the summer. But the other two show a new kind of vacation. It is often called an environmental vacation.

2   Some people take environmental vacations because they care about what is happening to the Earth. They want to learn what is wrong and try to help fix it. These people may find themselves counting elephants in Mali, watching birds in China, picking up garbage in Peru, collecting water samples from Lake Chad, or planting trees in Nepal. Often, they work beside people from those countries as well as others from all over the world. Making new friends is another benefit of environmental vacations.

3   An environmental vacation usually means hard work. Don't expect to be comfortable. If you can't stand mosquitoes biting you in your sleeping bag, stay home. If you don't like sleeping on the hard ground and eating food you've never tasted before, don't take an environmental vacation. So why would people spend summer after summer under conditions like these? As one person said, "I go because I believe it may be doing some good."

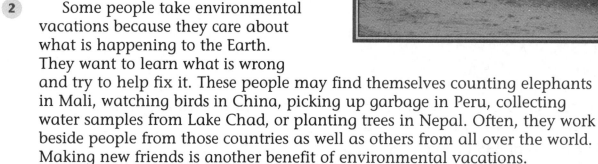

Circle the correct answer for questions 1–5.
Write your answer to question 6 on a separate piece of paper.

1. People take environmental vacations to _____.
   A get a good tan
   B eat strange food
   C try to help the planet
   D get rest and relaxation

2. Which word in paragraph 2 means "something that is good or helpful"?
   A trees
   B friends
   C benefit
   D garbage

3. What is the main idea of the article?
   A An environmental vacation is hard work.
   B A lot of high school students take environmental vacations.
   C Environmental vacations are a good way to make new friends.
   D Environmental vacations give people an opportunity to help the Earth while experiencing new people and places.

4. You can conclude from the article that people who take environmental vacations _____.
   A cannot afford typical vacations
   B only care about meeting new people
   C want to make the world a better place
   D are being punished for something they did wrong

5. *Common* can have the following meanings. Mark the meaning used in paragraph 1.
   A happening often
   B belonging to all
   C ordinary
   D average

6. What would be your ideal environmental vacation? Describe where you would go and what you would do.

Where did the guitar come from?

1   Picture this scene from prehistoric times. A band of hunters tracks game across a plain. When the sun is high in the sky, they stop to rest and eat. To entertain themselves they tap on logs or blow on grass stretched between their fingers. One hunter takes up his hunting bow and plucks the string. A pleasant twang comes out. Could the guitar have begun like this?

2   The hunting bow was used by almost every early culture. Over the years, it may have become the first stringed musical instrument as well. People of ancient Africa, the Middle East, and Greece all played stringed instruments. The North African Moors played the *ud* and brought it to Spain around A.D. 700. There, it probably mixed with the Greek *cithera* and the Middle Eastern *tanbur.* Out of this mix came the Spanish *guitarra.* Then, in the 1500s, the guitar made its way from Spain to the New World.

3   Soon, Africans were brought to the New World as slaves. They sang sad songs about their hard lives and strummed a stringed instrument called the banjo. Eventually, these African Americans began to strum guitars instead. Listening to their music in 1890, Czech composer Antonín Dvorák said that this would be the beginning of true American music. He was right. The sad songs became what people know as the blues, and the blues led to jazz and rock and roll. In each of these kinds of music, the guitar plays an important part.

Circle the correct answer for questions 1–5.
Write your answer to question 6 on a separate piece of paper.

1. The article does *not* tell _____.
   A about the earliest music
   B where the violin came from
   C where Antonín Dvorák was from
   D when the guitar first came to the New World

2. Which word in paragraph 3 means "person who writes musical works"?
   A banjo
   B guitar
   C composer
   D beginning

3. What happened before the guitar came from Spain to the New World?
   A Blues music began in America.
   B American slaves played the banjo.
   C The Moors brought the ud to Spain.
   D Africans were brought to the New World.

4. You can infer from the article that the guitar _____.
   A was invented in A.D. 700
   B is not used in jazz music
   C was influenced only by Spanish instruments
   D will continue to evolve in new and exciting ways

5. *Tracks* can have the following meanings. Mark the meaning used in paragraph 1.
   A footprints of an animal
   B paths made for racing
   C follows the traces of
   D courses of action

6. Write a short essay tracing the origin of the guitar to Africa.

What can be learned from garbage?

1.   Digging into garbage was homework for a class at the University of Arizona. Archaeologist William L. Rathje began this project in 1973. Usually, archaeologists dig up things left by ancient peoples. Rathje, on the other hand, decided to study what people had left behind last year or even last week.

2.   In the first part of the Garbage Project, students got permission to look through garbage cans of homes in Tucson. They wanted to find out if what people said they threw away matched what was in their garbage cans. For example, people said they ate a lot of cereals and few sweets. But their garbage cans often told a different story.

3.   Extending their study, students took samples from landfills in Arizona and other states. The samples, taken from 30 to 90 feet down, were put into recyclable or non-recyclable piles. Just as the students thought, people weren't recycling as much as they said. In fact, recyclable newspapers took up almost 18% of the space in landfills. Their condition was a surprise, too.

4.   Newspapers are biodegradable. This means they can be broken down into bits by bacteria. But newspapers from as far back as 40 years ago were almost as good as new. Landfills often just don't have enough oxygen to let the bacteria do their work. But since newspaper dates could still be read, students could date other items. They found that after 1983, when people began to think about their health, the amount of fat cut away from meat doubled from that cut off in earlier years.

5.   If you're an average American, you throw away about four pounds of garbage every day. You may not know it, but you could be leaving messages for future archaeologists.

Circle the correct answer for questions 1–5.
Write your answer to question 6 on a separate piece of paper.

1. The article does *not* tell _____.
   A when the Garbage Project began
   B where the Garbage Project began
   C what archaeologist began the project
   D which other states took part in the Garbage Project

2. Which word in paragraph 3 means "places where garbage is buried between layers of land"?
   A piles
   B samples
   C landfills
   D condition

3. Which paragraph tells how much garbage Americans throw away each day?
   A 2
   B 3
   C 4
   D 5

4. Why did newspapers in the landfill look so new?
   A There is not enough oxygen for bacteria to work.
   B They were not thrown out before the year 2000.
   C They were protected by layers of garbage.
   D They were protected by bacteria.

5. You can infer from the article that _____.
   A little can be learned from garbage
   B students hated the Garbage Project
   C people don't realize what they throw away
   D people in Tucson did a great job of recycling

6. Think about the garbage at your home. Write a plan for what and how you will be recycling.

Who is Carlos Santana?

1.   Carlos Santana was born to a musical family in Mexico in 1947. His father played the violin and tried to teach his five-year-old son to play. Carlos never became very good at playing the violin, though. Part of the problem was that he preferred rock and blues music to the Mexican mariachi music that his father played. Years later, he would change the sound of rock music.

2.   At the age of eight, Carlos began to play guitar. At 11, he was playing in popular nightclubs in Tijuana. Then his family moved to San Francisco. At first, Carlos was unhappy to leave behind the places where he played. After a while, though, he changed his mind. San Francisco had a large and eclectic music scene, including rock, jazz, folk, and salsa music.

3.   Carlos soon met other musicians. One of them was Jerry Garcia, who led a rock group named the Grateful Dead. Eventually, Carlos started his own group, Santana. By mixing rock and blues with a Latin beat, he started a new style of music called Latin Rock. Before long, his group had a hit album. In 1969, they played at the famous Woodstock music festival.

4.   Since then, Carlos has never stopped playing, although his music became less popular for a while. After his last big hit in 1982, radio stations stopped playing his songs. Then in 1998, he released an album titled *Supernatural*. It went back to his old sound but also included new influences like hip-hop. It sold 14 million copies and won eight Grammy awards. Carlos Santana has shown that his musical style can change with the times.

Circle the correct answer for questions 1–5.
Write your answer to question 6 on a separate piece of paper.

1. Carlos Santana first became interested in playing music because of _____.

   A the jazz musicians in San Francisco

   B the nightclubs in Tijuana

   C the Grateful Dead

   D his father

2. Which word in paragraph 2 means "varied"?

   A unhappy

   B popular

   C eclectic

   D though

3. Which paragraph tells what "Latin Rock" is?

   A 1

   B 2

   C 3

   D 4

4. What happened before Carlos Santana moved to San Francisco?

   A He met Jerry Garcia.

   B He played in nightclubs in Mexico.

   C He started the Latin Rock musical style.

   D He played at the Woodstock music festival.

5. You can infer from the article that _____.

   A Latin Rock no longer exists

   B Carlos Santana learned everything from his father

   C Carlos Santana owes his success to mixing different kinds of music

   D people stopped listening to Carlos Santana because he was from Mexico

6. If you were going to make a new kind of music, what would it sound like? How would it be influenced by kinds of music that are already around?

Can a butterfly cause a tornado?

1 Have you ever planned on doing something outside because the weather forecast said that it would be sunny? Did you look out the window in the morning only to see rain? This kind of thing happens a lot. Why is it so hard to predict the weather correctly?

2 Scientists who study the weather are called *meteorologists.* They are always trying to find ways of doing a better job. Other scientists, though, say that it is impossible to predict the weather accurately. This idea is based on chaos theory.

3 *Chaos* means a lack of order, but chaos theory does not say that there is no order in nature. Rather, it suggests that the order is so complicated that it *seems like* there is no order. There are simply too many factors that can influence the weather for accurate prediction to be possible.

4 Chaos theory is often explained by the butterfly effect. When a butterfly flaps its wings, it moves the air around it. That causes a tiny change in the atmosphere. This tiny change can cause larger changes. In time, these changes could build to the point that a tornado will destroy homes half a world away.

5 Chaos theory, then, says that to know exactly what the weather is going to be like next week, you would have to think about every pair of wings on Earth. Then, even if that were possible, there would be an infinite number of other factors. So, if tomorrow is supposed to be sunny, you might still want to take an umbrella along just in case.

Circle the correct answer for questions 1–5.
Write your answer to question 6 on a separate piece of paper.

1. Chaos theory does *not* say that _____.
   A people cannot know for sure what the weather will be like next week
   B a butterfly can cause a tornado
   C weather is very complicated
   D there is no order in nature

2. Which word in paragraph 5 means "countless"?
   A infinite
   B exactly
   C factors
   D every

3. Which paragraph tells the difference between *chaos* and *chaos theory?*
   A 1
   B 2
   C 3
   D 4

4. Why does chaos theory suggest that meteorology is so difficult?
   A Too many factors can influence the weather for accurate prediction.
   B Meteorologists are not knowledgeable about earth science.
   C Meteorologists are trying to do a better job.
   D Butterflies affect the atmosphere.

5. You can infer from the article that _____.
   A small actions in nature can have big effects
   B most tornadoes are caused by butterflies
   C weather is caused by magical forces
   D meteorologists are always accurate

6. Do you think that some small thing that you do could end up affecting things far away? Describe a chain of events beginning with yourself and ending with a big event.

What was Pompeii?

1   Pompeii is in southern Italy, near the Bay of Naples. It was once a busy town and favorite vacation spot for rich Romans. Today Pompeii still draws visitors. They wander through the streets, looking at maps and taking hundreds of pictures.

2   Like the faces in those photographs, Pompeii itself is frozen in time. Life there suddenly stopped on the 24th of August in A.D. 79. On that hot summer afternoon, a great roar filled the air. A mile away, Mount Vesuvius was erupting. As the frightened Pompeiians watched, a stream of rocks and ash began to pour down the volcano. In panic, the people ran from the city. The lucky ones escaped. But when the eruption was over, thousands of people had died. And Pompeii lay buried under 20 feet of ash.

3   For hundreds of years, Pompeii was ignored and almost completely forgotten. Then in the 1800s, trained workers began to uncover Pompeii's 160 acres block by block. Art, jewelry, and household goods were perfectly preserved by their blanket of ash. They looked as if they had been made yesterday. Records written on wax tablets and words written on walls could still be read. In a way, even the people came back to life. The shapes of their bodies had been pressed into the ash. Plaster was poured into these empty spaces. When it got hard, it showed perfectly the figures of Pompeiians who had been trapped more than 1,800 years before.

Circle the correct answer for questions 1–5.
Write your answer to question 6 on a separate piece of paper.

1. The article does *not* tell _____.

   A where Pompeii is

   B what Pompeii's houses were like

   C when workers began to uncover Pompeii

   D how much of Pompeii has been uncovered

2. Which word in paragraph 2 means "a sudden feeling of great fear"?

   A eruption

   B frozen

   C panic

   D roar

3. Why were the artifacts in Pompeii protected so well?

   A The lava didn't reach that part of town.

   B They were covered by a blanket of ash.

   C They were stored underground.

   D Italy went through an ice age.

4. You can infer from the article that _____.

   A there are still artifacts to be found underground in Pompeii

   B no written documents could be found in Pompeii

   C Pompeii has never grown beyond 160 acres

   D Mount Vesuvias erupts every few years

5. *Draws* can have the following meanings. Mark the meaning used in paragraph 1.

   A makes a picture

   B tie scores

   C attracts

   D inhales

6. Think about a natural disaster that has happened in your lifetime. What happened and what made the event so terrible? How did it affect you personally?

What is the most dangerous animal on Earth?

1   There are a number of candidates for the most dangerous animal on Earth. In the oceans, there are sharks. In many parts of the world, insects carry terrible diseases. In some places there are lions and tigers. The animal you would most want to avoid, though, may live in the far North.

2   Polar bears are Earth's largest meat eaters. An adult male can be up to 10 feet tall and weigh up to 1,700 pounds. They eat seals, but also sometimes they will enjoy a tasty walrus or beluga whale. A polar bear's diet is not limited to these animals, though. Lions and tigers will not go after humans unless they are very hungry and people happen to come wandering along. A polar bear, on the other hand, will not hesitate to stalk people like any other prey.

3   To make matters worse, a polar bear's sense of smell is 100 times stronger than a human's. So, a bear can smell you from miles away. Then, it can run 40 miles per hour after you. Plus, polar bears are excellent swimmers and have small bumps on their paws called *papillae* to keep from slipping on the ice while chasing you.

4   The good news is that you are not likely to run into a polar bear unless you live above the Arctic Circle. Also, while they *can* eat people, they rarely do. In fact, today, the fearsome polar bear may itself be endangered.

5   How can that be? Because of air pollution, poaching, and rising temperatures, the polar bear population has been dropping each year. The polar bear is threatened by what is truly the most dangerous animal on Earth: humans.

Circle the correct answer for questions 1–5.
Write your answer to question 6 on a separate piece of paper.

1. The article does *not* say that polar bears eat _____.

   A seals

   B walruses

   C penguins

   D beluga whales

2. Which word in paragraph 2 means "hunt"?

   A eat

   B prey

   C stalk

   D hesitate

3. Which paragraph tells how big polar bears are?

   A 1

   B 2

   C 3

   D 4

4. You can conclude from the article that _____.

   A people are a bigger threat to polar bears than polar bears are to people

   B a person can probably outrun a polar bear on the right terrain

   C polar bears are smaller than lions

   D polar bears eat lots of people

5. *Diet* can have the following meanings. Mark the meaning used in paragraph 2.

   A something provided habitually

   B cutting down on what is eaten

   C food regularly consumed

   D plan to lose weight

6. Imagine that you are hiking above the Arctic Circle. Write a journal entry about your experience traveling through polar bear country.

What is the American Indian Dance Theatre?

1.   The American Indian Dance Theatre brings the colorful, ancient dances of Native American cultures to people everywhere. Here's what you might see at a show. The curtain opens on a woman in a purple, red, and yellow butterfly headdress. She begins to leap across the stage. The fringe on her beautiful dress swings as she moves. This is the Butterfly Dance of the Zuni Indians. The Zunis honor this insect because it carries pollen to make new plants each year.

2.   Next comes the Apache Crown Dance. Blazing in bright red light, a masked man becomes a mountain spirit. He dances to help the sick get well. At his side dances a clown. The clown explains with his hands what the mountain spirit is doing. Huge bird masks cover the heads of the next two dancers. They perform the Hamatsa Dance of the Kwakiutl. It tells the story of a youth who gets into trouble for not following the rules of his tribe.

3.   Music played on a wooden flute signals the start of the Eagle Dance of the Plains tribes. Dancers wearing feathered capes soar and wheel around the stage. They act out the life of the eagle. This bird is very special to the Plains tribes. It is believed to carry messages between people and their creator.

4.   Finally comes one of the most difficult dances. A Cherokee dancer takes the stage. He twists and turns 36 beaded hoops around his body until they take the shapes of a snake, a flower, and an eagle. To end the show, he uses his whole body to turn the hoops into a globe. This represents the Earth, home of all the tribes.

5.   Founded in 1987, the American Indian Dance Theatre tours the world, sharing the music and movement of a vibrant culture. The group will celebrate the rich history of Native American cultures for many years to come.

Circle the correct answer for questions 1–5.
Write your answer to question 6 on a separate piece of paper.

1. The dance in which a mountain spirit helps the sick is the _____.
   A Eagle Dance
   B Hamatsa Dance
   C Dance of the Zunis
   D Apache Crown Dance

2. Which word in paragraph 1 means "customs, beliefs, and arts of groups of people"?
   A fringe
   B dances
   C curtain
   D cultures

3. Which paragraph tells about the dance of the Kwakiutl tribe?
   A 1
   B 2
   C 3
   D 4

4. What dance is described third in the article?
   A Eagle Dance
   B Butterfly Dance
   C Hamatsa Dance
   D Apache Crown Dance

5. You can infer from the article that _____.
   A Native Americans don't like to dance
   B the Eagle Dance is the most beautiful
   C dancing helps teach others about Native American cultures
   D the costumes of the American Indian Dance Theatre are not realistic

6. Describe a dance that represents your own culture. What movements does it have?

How can you save a choking person's life?

1. You're sharing pizza with a friend. The two of you are having a good time, talking and laughing. Suddenly, your friend is quiet. There's a frightened look on his face. He grasps his throat. What can you do?

2. The Heimlich maneuver can save your friend. And this procedure is easy to learn. Here's what to do. First, quickly ask him if he can speak or cough. A shake of his head will let you know that this really is an emergency. That bite of pizza blocking his airway must be removed!

3. Stand behind your friend and wrap your arms around his waist. Make a fist with one hand and grab that hand just above the wrist with your other hand. Place your fist in the middle of your friend's body, with your thumb just above the navel. Make a firm, quick thrust into the stomach area, pressing inward and upward. Do this a few times. Your thrusts will force air upward from your friend's lungs. That air should push the pizza from his airway so he can breathe again.

4. And what if *you* are the one choking? The most important step is to let someone know. Grab your throat and point to get attention. Some people have choked to death because they were too shy or embarrassed to call for help. If you are alone and choking, your only chance may be to stay calm and try to use the Heimlich maneuver on yourself.

5. Hundreds of people, from small children to movie stars, have used the Heimlich maneuver to save lives. If you know what to do, you can be a life saver, too.

Circle the correct answer for questions 1–5.
Write your answer to question 6 on a separate piece of paper.

1. The article does *not* tell _____.
   A who Heimlich is
   B what to do if you start to choke
   C how to force air up from the lungs
   D where to stand when using the maneuver

2. Which word in paragraph 2 means "a planned movement"?
   A cough
   B airway
   C emergency
   D maneuver

3. Which paragraph tells the first thing to do when someone looks like he or she is choking?
   A 1
   B 2
   C 3
   D 4

4. What forces air upward into a person's lungs?
   A breathing into the person's mouth
   B thrusting inward and upward on the stomach
   C wrapping your arms around the person's waist
   D placing your fist in the middle of the person's body

5. You can infer from the article that _____.
   A the Heimlich maneuver is painful
   B it's hard to do the Heimlich maneuver
   C you have to be certified to do the Heimlich maneuver
   D you don't have to be strong to use the Heimlich maneuver

6. Have you ever experienced a medical emergency? Describe what you did.

Who was Bertha von Suttner?

1 Chances are you've never heard of Bertha von Suttner. Not many people have. But she was an important figure in the history of pacifism, the struggle to stop war and keep peace. Von Suttner also helped bring about one of the most famous prizes in the world, the Nobel Peace Prize.

2 Bertha von Suttner was born in 1843. As she grew up, she realized that the world was not a perfect place. Many wars were being fought, and people were dying senselessly. Von Suttner wanted to stop all that. She studied the current wars and fighting. With all that she learned, she wrote a novel called *Lay Down Your Arms*. Many people read von Suttner's novel.

3 But von Suttner didn't stop there. She wrote and wrote about why peace was better than war. She traveled far and wide to convince people to "lay down their arms." She became famous for her position against war.

4 In her travels, von Suttner met many important people. One of the first of those people was Alfred Nobel. Nobel was a scientist who was developing explosives for war and railroads. He, too, was a pacifist, but a different sort of pacifist. He wanted to scare people out of war and into peace by making the most horrible, destructive weapon anyone could imagine. When people saw how awful the weapon was, they would be too frightened to fight. Wars would come to an end.

5 Though they had their differences, von Suttner and Nobel became lifelong friends. Nobel came to many of von Suttner's peace meetings, and he gave some of his sizable wealth to her peace organizations. Eventually, von Suttner convinced Nobel to establish a fund for a yearly peace prize. The prize was first awarded in 1901. Von Suttner herself won the Nobel Peace Prize in 1905.

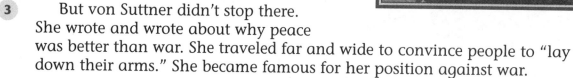

Circle the correct answer for questions 1–5.
Write your answer to question 6 on a separate piece of paper.

1. Bertha von Suttner wanted to put an end to _____.
   A the Nobel Prize
   B novels
   C peace
   D war

2. What word in paragraph 2 means "in the same time or age"?
   A senselessly
   B current
   C perfect
   D many

3. Which paragraph tells about Alfred Nobel's ideas about peace?
   A 1
   B 2
   C 3
   D 4

4. What happened first in Bertha von Suttner's life?
   A She wrote a novel.
   B She met Alfred Nobel.
   C She studied wars and fighting.
   D She won the Nobel Peace Prize.

5. You can conclude from the article that Alfred Nobel _____.
   A liked war
   B was not charitable
   C did not like Bertha von Suttner
   D was influenced by Bertha von Suttner

6. Use print and online resources to learn about the life of Alfred Nobel. Write a short biography of his life.

Are you a "lefty" or a "righty"?

1 Get a piece of paper and a pencil. Write down your name. If you are like 90% of Americans, you hold the pencil in your right hand. The other 10%, left-handers, know how difficult living in a right-handed world can be. Almost everything, from scissors to guitars to TV remote controls, is made for right-handers.

2 The hand you are most likely to use is called your dominant hand. You have probably been aware of this since you were very young. But you may not know that you also have a foot, eye, and side of your brain that are dominant.

3 Finding out if you are left-footed or right-footed is easy. Just pretend to kick a ball. There's a test for the eyes, too. Hold one arm straight out from the middle of your body. Point your index finger so it blocks something in the distance. Look at the finger with both eyes open. Then close one eye at a time. If, for example, your finger seems to stay in the same place when you look at it with only your left eye, you are left-eyed.

4 Finding which side of your brain is dominant is a little harder. It depends on how you hold your pencil. Is your hand straight, with the pencil pointing away from you? Or is it hooked, with the pencil pointing toward you? Straight right-handers and hooked left-handers are left-brained. Straight left-handers and hooked right-handers have a dominant right brain.

5 Here's one more experiment with right and left. This one is just for fun, though. On a picture of your face, put the edge of an unframed mirror along the nose. What do you notice when you look at the picture from the right and then from the left?

Circle the correct answer for questions 1–5.
Write your answer to question 6 on a separate piece of paper.

1. About _____ of Americans are left-handed.

   A 40%

   B 30%

   C 20%

   D 10%

2. Which word in paragraph 3 means "something used to show what other things are like"?

   A example

   B middle

   C finger

   D index

3. Which paragraph tells why life is difficult for left-handed people?

   A 1

   B 2

   C 3

   D 4

4. In the eye test described in the article, if your finger stays the same when you look at it only with your right eye, you are _____.

   A left-eyed

   B right-eyed

   C nearsighted

   D right-handed

5. *Remote* can have the following meanings. Mark the meaning used in paragraph 1.

   A out of the way

   B small in degree

   C operated from a distance

   D far removed in space or time

6. Read the last paragraph of the article again. What do you think you'd see? Why? Try the experiment and describe what happens.

What was the Donner party?

1.   Many tales are told about the hardships faced by the pioneers who settled the West. None is sadder than the story of the Donner party.

2.   During the winter of 1846, George Donner was leading 87 settlers across the Sierra Nevada mountains into California. In his group were 39 children, most of them under 6 years old. Even though it was still early in November, unusually heavy storms hit the mountains. The Donner party was trapped in a high pass. Snow blocked the pass in both directions. It was impossible to keep going ahead or to turn back.

3.   Some men and women decided to leave the group. They were going to try to find a way down the mountain. Seven of them were able to get to Sutter's Fort, which is now Sacramento. Four rescue teams were sent out from there to search for the snowbound Donner party. Meanwhile, the settlers were dying from cold and hunger. Desperate to survive, the pioneers turned to their last source of food—the bodies of their dead.

4.   In March, rescue workers finally reached what was left of the Donner party. Only 40 people had survived. They were carried down from the mountains. Newspaper stories noted that few of the children had died. Apparently, many of the adults had given up their own lives so that the children would have food.

5.   Today, the pass where so many lives were lost is called Donner Pass. It is a national landmark. It helps people remember the ordeal of the Donner party during that terrible winter.

Circle the correct answer for questions 1–5.
Write your answer to question 6 on a separate piece of paper.

1. The article does *not* tell _____.

   A why the Donner party was trapped

   B where the Donner party was going

   C whether George Donner survived

   D where Donner Pass is

2. Which word in paragraph 5 means "a very difficult or painful experience"?

   A landmark

   B ordeal

   C winter

   D lives

3. Which paragraph tells when the Donner party was found?

   A 1

   B 2

   C 3

   D 4

4. Why were so many children in the Donner party found alive?

   A Adults had given up their lives to save them.

   B Their bodies were better prepared for cold.

   C Almost all the 87 settlers were children.

   D Rescue workers reached them first.

5. *Pass* can have the following meanings. Mark the meaning used in paragraph 2.

   A narrow road or path

   B render a decision

   C free ticket

   D go by

6. Was George Donner wise to try to cross the mountains in early November? Why or why not?

How has an Incan secret changed cotton?

1   A student traveling in Peru in 1981 liked the clothing worn by Indians there. Their cotton shirts and skirts were soft and had lovely colors in brown, tan, and light green. The student was surprised to learn that the people had not used dyes on the cloth. Their cotton just grew that way—in color! The student decided to bring some of the material back to the United States.

2   Sally Fox, a scientist who studied insects, heard about colored cotton. In her free time, Fox liked to spin cotton by hand. She wanted to try colored cotton, so she planted seeds of the Peruvian plant. To her surprise, the cotton plants grew in more colors. Some were even light pink.

3   Fox was quick to see how naturally colored cotton could help the environment. For one thing, fewer dyes would be needed. That would keep some pollution out of our waters. Another plus was that, unlike white cotton, colored cotton wouldn't be ruined by green stains from its own leaves during harvest. That meant that the leaves would no longer have to be stripped off by harmful chemicals before harvest. Finally, the cotton from Peru, which the Incas had grown there for thousands of years, was naturally strong. It resisted insects. So here was a chance to get rid of chemical bug sprays, too.

4   Sally Fox's work in cotton breeding has grown into a 40-acre enterprise, Natural Cotton Colours, Inc., which has expanded the range of natural cotton clothing and home products available throughout the world. Clothing manufacturers who care about the environment hope that Fox and other cotton farmers will someday be able to grow the plant in every color of the rainbow.

Circle the correct answer for questions 1–5.
Write your answer to question 6 on a separate piece of paper.

1. Colored cotton was found in _____.

   A Peru

   B Chile

   C Mexico

   D New Mexico

2. Which word in paragraph 3 means "didn't give in to the attacks of"?

   A stripped

   B colored

   C resisted

   D ruined

3. Which paragraph tells why colored cotton is good for the environment?

   A 1

   B 2

   C 3

   D 4

4. Why would leaves no longer have to be stripped off during the harvest of colored cotton?

   A The leaves are mixed with the cotton to give it color.

   B Colored cotton wouldn't be ruined by green stains.

   C Colored cotton would be ruined by chemicals.

   D The leaves help the cotton resist insects.

5. You can infer from the article that colored cotton _____.

   A cannot be dyed

   B is more difficult to pick

   C is not used for sweaters

   D does not grow in strong colors like red or purple

6. Some people who suffer from allergies are glad to wear clothes made from colored cotton. Explain why the colored cotton is helpful for them.